Financial statements

Workbook

David Cox

Published by Osborne Books Limited
Unit 1B Everoak Estate
Bromyard Road, Worcester WR2 5HP
Tel 01905 748071
Email books@osbornebooks.co.uk
Website www.osbornebooks.co.uk

Design by Laura Ingham

Printed by CPI Group (UK) Limited, Croydon, CR0 4YY, on environmentally friendly, acid-free paper from managed forests.

British Library Cataloguing in Publication Data
A catalogue record for this book is available from the British Library

ISBN 978 1909173 262

Contents

Introduction

Acknowledgements

The author wishes to thank the following for their help with the production of the book: Jean Cox, Maz Loton and Cathy Turner. Thanks are also due to Alison Aplin for her technical editing and to Laura Ingham for her designs for this new series.

The publisher is indebted to the Association of Accounting Technicians for its help and advice to our authors and editors during the preparation of this text.

Author

David Cox is a Certified Accountant with more than twenty years' experience teaching accountancy students over a wide range of levels. Formerly with the Management and Professional Studies Department at Worcester College of Technology, he now lectures on a freelance basis and carries out educational consultancy work in accountancy studies. He is author and joint author of a number of textbooks in the areas of accounting, finance and banking.

Introduction

what this book covers

This book has been written to cover the 'Financial statements' Unit which is mandatory for the revised (2013) AAT Level 4 Diploma in Accounting.

what this book contains

This book is set out in two sections:

■ **Chapter Activities** which provide extra practice material in addition to the activities included in the Osborne Books Tutorial text. Answers to the Chapter activities are included in this book.

■ **Practice Assessments** are provided to prepare the student for the Computer Based Assessments. They are based directly on the structure, style and content of the sample assessment material provided by the AAT at www.aat.org.uk. Suggested answers to the Practice Assessments are set out in this book.

year dates, negative amounts

Note that year dates are shown in the book as either 20-1 or 20X1; negative money amounts are shown with either brackets, eg (£1,000), or with a minus sign, eg –£1,000.

further information

If you want to know more about our products and resources, please visit www.osbornebooks.co.uk for further details and access to our online shop.

Chapter activities

1 Purpose of financial statements

1.1 **(a)** What is the objective of financial statements according to the *Conceptual Framework for Financial Reporting*?

(b) For the three user groups identified in the *Conceptual Framework for Financial Reporting*, identify their purposes in using financial reporting information.

1.2 Which one of the following statements is correct?

	✔
income − expenses = profits or losses	
assets − expenses = profits or losses	
assets + expenses = profits or losses	
income + expenses = profits or losses	

1.3 Which one of the following options is correct?

Assets £	Liabilities £	Equity £	✔
20,600	8,350	28,950	
16,850	7,950	7,900	
18,550	8,200	10,530	
35,250	14,600	20,650	

1.4 The *Conceptual Framework for Financial Reporting* identifies four enhancing qualitative characteristics that make the information provided in financial statements useful to users.

Write in the enhancing qualitative characteristic that relates to each of the statements below.

Statement	Characteristic
Financial information that is available to decision-makers in time to be capable in influencing their decisions	
Financial information that helps assure users that information is faithfully represented	
Users of financial statements are able to identify and understand similarities in, and differences among, items	
Users of financial statements are presented with information that is classified and characterised clearly and concisely	

1.5 **(a)** Set out the accounting equation and define the elements in the equation.

(b) Briefly explain how profit for the year affects the elements of the accounting equation.

1.6 **(a)** What are the elements that appear in financial statements according to the *Conceptual Framework for Financial Reporting*?

(b) Define the elements that appear in the statement of profit or loss and other comprehensive income in accordance with the definitions in the *Conceptual Framework for Financial Reporting*.

2 Introduction to limited company financial statements

- Blank photocopiable pro-formas in the format used in AAT Assessments – of the statement of profit or loss and other comprehensive income and the statement of financial position, are included in the Appendix – it is advisable to enlarge them to full A4 size. Blank workings sheets are also included in the Appendix.

- Pro-formas and workings sheets are also available to download from www.osbornebooks.co.uk.

2.1 **(a)** Define a public limited company (plc)

(b) Define a private limited company (ltd)

2.2 What is meant by a limited company having a separate legal entity?

	✔
The name of the company is different from that of the individual shareholders	
Anyone taking legal action proceeds against the company and not the individual shareholders	
In the event of the company becoming insolvent, the shareholders can only lose the amount of their investment	
The directors manage the company on behalf of shareholders	

2.3 Which one of the following investments in a company usually carries voting rights at meetings of the company?

	✔
Ordinary shares	
Preference shares	
Debentures	
Long-term loans	

2.4 A new company issues 100,000 ordinary shares of 50p each at a premium of 10 per cent. What amount will be shown as the total of the equity section of the company's statement of financial position?

	✔
£100,000	
£110,000	
£50,000	
£55,000	

2.5 Crantock plc prepares its financial statements to 31 March each year. At 31 March 20-2 its trial balance was as follows:

	£000	£000
Administrative expenses	240	
Share capital		700
Trade and other receivables	525	
Cash and cash equivalents	75	
Share premium		200
Distribution costs	500	
Plant and equipment at cost	1,600	
Accumulated depreciation on plant and equipment		500
Retained earnings at 1 April 20-1		350
Purchases	1,200	
Inventories at 1 April 20-1	160	
Trade and other payables		395
Sales revenue		2,295
Dividends paid	140	
	4,440	4,440

Further information:

- Inventories at 31 March 20-2 cost £180,000.

- The corporation tax charge for the year has been calculated as £65,000.

- Depreciation on plant and equipment has already been provided for in the list of balances above and allocated to distribution costs and administrative expenses accordingly.

Required:

Prepare the financial statements of Crantock plc for the year ended 31 March 20-2.

2.6 Playfair Ltd prepares its financial statements to 31 December each year. At 31 December 20-3 its trial balance was as follows:

	£000	£000
Share capital		580
Share premium		50
Land at cost	500	
Plant and equipment at cost	800	
Trade receivables	350	
Trade payables		160
Accruals		30
Prepayments	40	
Cash and cash equivalents	140	
Bank loans (non-current)		200
Inventories at 1 January 20-3	250	
Administrative expenses	110	
Purchases	1,650	
Sales revenue		2,340
Debenture interest paid	20	
Distribution costs	240	
Accumulated depreciation on plant and equipment		230
Dividends paid	50	
Retained earnings at 1 January 20-3		540
Allowance for doubtful debts at 1 January 20-3		20
	4,150	4,150

Further information:

- Inventories at 31 December 20-3 cost £280,000

- Depreciation of plant and equipment is to be charged at the rate of 20 per cent per annum on cost and allocated equally between distribution costs and administrative expenses

- The allowance for doubtful debts is to be increased to £40,000

- Interest on the bank loans has not been paid for the second half of the year; the interest due amounts to £20,000

- The corporation tax charge for the year has been calculated as £30,000

Required:

Prepare the financial statements of Playfair Ltd for the year to 31 December 20-3.

3 Published financial statements of limited companies

- Blank photocopiable pro-formas in the format used in AAT Assessments – of the statement of profit or loss and other comprehensive income, the statement of changes in equity, and the statement of financial position, are included in the Appendix – it is advisable to enlarge them to full A4 size. Blank workings sheets are also included in the Appendix.

- Pro-formas and workings sheets are also available to download from www.osbornebooks.co.uk.

3.1 Complete the following sentence taken from IAS 1, *Presentation of Financial Statements*:

'The objective of financial statements is to provide .... about the

.... position, financial .... and ....

flows of an entity that is .... to a wide range of .... in

making .... decisions.'

Choose from the following words:

    cash

    economic

    financial

    information

    performance

    useful

    users

3.2 Under IAS 1, *Presentation of Financial Statements*, which of the following is included in a complete set of financial statements?

1.   statement of profit or loss and other comprehensive income

2.   statement of cash flows

3.   directors' report

4.   statement of changes in equity

	✔
1 and 2	
1, 2 and 3	
1, 2 and 4	
all of them	

3.3   What are the deadlines for filing the statutory accounts with the Registrar of Companies for (1) a private limited company and (2) a public limited company?

		✔
(1) nine months	(2) nine months	
(1) six months	(2) six months	
(1) six months	(2) nine months	
(1) nine months	(2) six months	

3.4   Which of the following is included under the heading for 'Equity' in a statement of financial position?
1.   revaluation reserve
2.   bank loans
3.   share premium
4.   long-term provisions

	✔
1 and 2	
1, 2 and 3	
1 and 3	
all of them	

3.5   Which of the following involves a cash flow?
1.   a rights issue of shares
2.   the revaluation of a non-current asset
3.   depreciation of non-current assets
4.   a bonus issue of shares

	✔
1	
1 and 2	
1, 2 and 3	
all of them	

3.6 You have been asked to help prepare the financial statements of Wymark Ltd for the year ended 31 March 20X4. The company's trial balance as at 31 March 20X4 and further information is shown below.

Wymark Ltd

Trial balance as at 31 March 20X4

	Debit	Credit
	£000	£000
Share capital		3,500
Prepayments	42	
Trade and other payables		1,309
Land and buildings – value/cost	5,000	
– accumulated depreciation at 1 April 20X3		702
Plant and equipment – cost	2,722	
– accumulated depreciation at 1 April 20X3		1,402
Trade and other receivables	1,802	
Accruals		105
8% bank loan repayable 20X9		2,500
Cash and cash equivalents	155	
Retained earnings at 1 April 20X3		1,457
Interest paid	200	
Sales revenue		10,884
Purchases	7,854	
Distribution costs	980	
Administrative expenses	461	
Inventories at 1 April 20X3	2,043	
Dividends paid	600	
	21,859	21,859

Further information:

- The inventories at the close of business on 31 March 20X4 cost £2,422,000.

- Land, which is not depreciated, is included in the trial balance at a value of £3,500,000. It is to be revalued at £4,000,000 and this revaluation is to be included in the financial statements for the year ended 31 March 20X4.

- Depreciation is to be provided for the year to 31 March 20X4 as follows:

    Buildings   2% per annum   Straight-line basis

    Plant and equipment   25% per annum   Reducing (diminishing) balance basis

- Depreciation is to be apportioned as follows:

	%
Cost of sales	50
Distribution costs	30
Administrative expenses	20

- Trade receivables include a debt of £11,000 which is to be written off. Bad (irrecoverable) debts are to be classified as administrative expenses.

- Distribution costs of £12,000 owing at 31 March 20X4 are to be provided for.

- The corporation tax charge for the year has been calculated as £348,000.

- All of the operations are continuing operations.

Required:

(a) Draft the statement of profit or loss and other comprehensive income for Wymark Ltd for the year ended 31 March 20X4.

(b) Draft the statement of changes in equity for Wymark Ltd for the year ended 31 March 20X4.

(c) Draft the statement of financial position for Wymark Ltd as at 31 March 20X4.

3.7   You have been asked to help prepare the financial statements of Nathan Ltd for the year ended 31 March 20X1. The company's trial balance as at 31 March 20X1 and further information is shown below.

Nathan Ltd

Trial balance as at 31 March 20X1

	Debit	Credit
	£000	£000
Share capital		6,000
Share premium		1,000
Trade and other payables		1,010
Prepayments	186	
Returns outwards		47
Plant and equipment – cost	20,500	
– accumulated depreciation at 1 April 20X0		4,600
Trade and other receivables	1,546	
Accruals		85
5% bank loan repayable 20X8		3,000
Cash and cash equivalents	110	
Retained earnings at 1 April 20X0		2,537
Interest paid	150	
Sales revenue		21,495
Purchases	9,364	
Distribution costs	3,852	
Administrative expenses	2,975	
Inventories at 1 April 20X0	641	
Dividends paid	450	
	39,774	39,774

Further information:

- The inventories at the close of business on 31 March 20X1 cost £627,000.
- Depreciation is to be provided on plant and equipment for the year to 31 March 20X1 at 25% per annum using the reducing (diminishing) balance basis. Depreciation is to be apportioned 60% to distribution costs and 40% to administrative expenses.
- Trade receivables include a debt of £12,000 which is to be written off. Bad (irrecoverable) debts are to be classified as administrative expenses.
- Distribution costs of £22,000 owing at 31 March 20X1 are to be provided for.
- The corporation tax charge for the year has been calculated as £207,000.
- All of the operations are continuing operations.

Required:

(a)   Draft the statement of profit or loss and other comprehensive income for Nathan Ltd for the year ended 31 March 20X1.

(b)   Draft the statement of changes in equity for Nathan Ltd for the year ended 31 March 20X1.

(c)   Draft the statement of financial position for Nathan Ltd as at 31 March 20X1.

4 Accounting for assets

4.1 Task 1

What are the two criteria stated by IAS 16, *Property, Plant and Equipment*, for an item of PPE to be recognised as an asset?

Task 2

IAS 16 states that, initially, PPE are measured at cost on the statement of financial position.

(a) Explain what is meant by 'cost'

(b) State two attributable costs which **can be included** in the cost of an asset

(c) State two costs which **cannot be included** in the cost of an asset

(d) Briefly explain the two models from which an entity must choose as its accounting policy after acquisition of PPE

4.2 With reference to IAS 16, *Property, Plant and Equipment*, you are to:

(a) Define depreciation.

(b) Summarise the points a company must consider when accounting for IAS 16.

4.3 According to IAS 38, *Intangible Assets*, which one of the following is not a criteria for capitalising development costs by a business entity?

	✔
The entity intends to complete the intangible asset and to use or sell it	
The entity has no specific aim or application for the intangible asset	
The entity has the resources available to complete the development and to use or sell the intangible asset	
The entity has the ability to measure the development expenditure reliably	

4.4   IAS 38, *Intangible Assets*, gives three key elements of an intangible asset. Which one of the following is not one of the three key elements?

	✔
Reliability	
Identifiability	
Control	
Future economic benefits	

4.5   The directors of Tanhosier Ltd are about to undertake the development of a new product. They expect the costs of development to be significant and are concerned at the impact that this might have on their financial statements.

You have been asked to prepare notes to deal with the following queries of the directors:

(a)   What is an intangible asset?

(b)   What would have to be demonstrated by Tanhosier Ltd before an intangible asset arising from development is recognised as an intangible asset in the financial statements?

4.6   To which of the following assets does IAS 36, *Impairment of Assets*, apply?
1   land and buildings
2   inventories
3   goodwill
4   vehicles

	✔
all of them	
1 and 2	
1, 2 and 3	
1, 3 and 4	

4.7   **Task 1**

Identify *two* external and *two* internal indicators of impairment.

Task 2

(a)   Explain what is meant by an impairment review.

(b)   How is an impairment review carried out?

4.8   A business has four assets which the directors wish to test for impairment:

asset	carrying amount	fair value, less costs of disposal	value in use
	£	£	£
1	12,000	11,000	10,000
2	8,000	8,000	9,000
3	15,000	12,000	14,000
4	17,000	19,000	18,000

Which of the above assets is impaired according to IAS 36, *Impairment of Assets*?

	✔
1	
2	
1 and 3	
2 and 4	

4.9   Interest of £4,500 on a finance lease is to be apportioned over the lease term of five years from 20-1 to 20-5. State the finance charge amounts that will be debited to each year's statement of profit or loss and other comprehensive income using the-sum-of-the-digits method.

Year	Finance charge £
20-1	
20-2	
20-3	
20-4	
20-5	

4.10 **(a)** Explain the two inventory valuation methods allowed by IAS 2, *Inventories*.

(b) Which method of inventory valuation cannot be used under IAS 2?

4.11 Which one of the following statements best describes the valuation of inventories under IAS 2, *Inventories* at the end of the financial year?

✔

At the lower of FIFO and AVCO	
At the lower of cost and net realisable value	
At the higher of FIFO and AVCO	
At the higher of cost and net realisable value	

4.12 You have been asked to assist the directors of Lawnderer Limited, a company that markets and distributes lawnmowers and other garden machinery, in the preparation of the financial statements for the year ended 30 September 20-5.

The directors of the company have had a meeting with you regarding the possible treatment of certain future expenditure in the financial statements of the company. They have told you that the company has been approached by an inventor who has an idea to develop a revolutionary new lawnmower. The project looks technically feasible and preliminary marketing studies suggest a significant market for that product. Cost and revenue projections suggest that future profits should adequately cover the cost of development and have a beneficial effect on the future profitability of the company. The directors are concerned about the effect that the expenditure on developing the new product will have on future profits, given that it will take some time between commencing the project and commercial production.

Task

Explain how the costs of developing the new lawnmower will be reflected in the future financial statements of the company.

5 Accounting for liabilities and the statement of profit or loss

5.1 Barrios Limited has a corporation tax charge of £25,000 based on its profits for the current year. Where is this recognised in the year end financial statements?

	✔
In the statement of profit or loss and other comprehensive income only	
In the statement of profit or loss and other comprehensive income and as a non-current liability in the statement of financial position	
In the statement of profit or loss and other comprehensive income and as a current liability in the statement of financial position	
As a current liability in the statement of financial position only	

5.2 Under IAS 17, *Leases*, how should finance leases be recognised as liabilities on a lessee's statement of financial position?

	✔
At the lower of cost and net realisable value of the asset being leased	
At the lower of the fair value of the asset being leased and the present value of the minimum lease payments	
At the higher of the fair value of the asset being leased and its value in use	
At the carrying amount of the asset being leased	

5.3 With reference to IAS 37, *Provisions, Contingent Liabilities and Contingent Assets*, you are to:

(a) Define

- provisions
- contingent liabilities
- contingent assets

(b) Explain for each the accounting treatment, if any, in the year end financial statements.

5.4 A business prepares its financial statements to 31 December each year. The following events took place after 31 December but before the date on which the financial statements were authorised for issue:

1. a significant part of the business is to be discontinued

2. the net realisable value of inventories is found to be materially below the cost price used in the financial statements

Which of the above is likely to be classified as an adjusting event under IAS 10, *Events after the Reporting Period*?

	✔
1 only	
2 only	
1 and 2	
neither 1 nor 2	

5.5 A major customer who owes money to a company at the end of the financial year is declared bankrupt before the date of authorising the financial statements for issue. Under IAS 10, *Events after the Reporting Period*, this should be classified as an adjusting event.

	✔
True	
False	

5.6   Prepare notes for a meeting with the directors of Cortez Limited to explain the accounting treatment of the following issues:

    (a)   A note to the accounts states that there was a fire in the warehouse of the company that occurred after the year end and resulted in considerable losses of non-current assets and inventories. No adjustment for these losses appears to have been made in the year end financial statements.

    (b)   There is a non-current liability for something called a 'finance lease' in the statement of financial position of the company.

    Note: You should make reference, where appropriate, to relevant international financial reporting standards.

5.7   With reference to IAS 18, *Revenue*, you are to:

    (a)   Explain what is meant by revenue. Give two examples of revenue, other than the sale of goods.

    (b)   State how revenue is to be measured.

    (c)   Explain when revenue from the sale of goods should be recognised.

6   Statement of cash flows

- A blank photocopiable pro-forma in the format used in AAT Assessments – of the statement of cash flows, is included in the Appendix – it is advisable to enlarge it to full A4 size. Blank workings sheets are also included in the Appendix.

- Pro-formas and workings sheets are also available to download from www.osbornebooks.co.uk.

6.1   Rowan Ltd has a profit from operations of £30,000 for the year and the statement of profit or loss and statement of financial position show the following:

	£
depreciation charge	10,000
increase in inventories	5,000
decrease in trade and other receivables	4,000
increase in trade and other payables	6,000

What is the cash from operations for the year?

	✔
£45,000 inflow	
£15,000 inflow	
£55,000 inflow	
£25,000 inflow	

6.2 Meadow Ltd has a loss from operations of £10,000 for the year and the statement of profit or loss and statement of financial position show the following:

	£
depreciation charge	8,000
decrease in inventories	4,000
increase in trade and other receivables	5,000
decrease in trade and other payables	3,000

What is the cash from operations for the year?

	✔
£14,000 inflow	
£30,000 inflow	
£14,000 outflow	
£6,000 outflow	

6.3 Boughton Ltd has the following items of receipts and payments for the year:

1. cash received from sales
2. cash paid to suppliers and employees
3. interest paid
4. tax paid
5. cash received from share issue

How is the cash from operating activities calculated using the direct method?

	✔
1 + 2 − 3 − 4 + 5	
1 − 2 + 3 − 4	
1 − 2 − 3 − 4	
1 − 2 + 3 + 4 + 5	

6.4 You have been asked to help prepare the statement of cash flows and statement of changes in equity for Carmen Ltd for the year ended 31 March 20X1.

The most recent statement of profit or loss and statement of financial position (with comparatives for the previous year) of Carmen Ltd are set out below.

Carmen Ltd – Statement of profit or loss for the year ended 31 March 20X1

	£000
Continuing operations	
Revenue	33,040
Cost of sales	–14,270
Gross profit	18,770
Dividends received	30
Loss on disposal of property, plant and equipment	–50
Distribution costs	–10,210
Administrative expenses	–6,340
Profit from operations	2,200
Finance costs	–190
Profit before tax	2,010
Tax	–350
Profit for the year from continuing operations	1,660

	20X1 £000	20X0 £000
Assets		
Non-current assets		
Property, plant and equipment	15,350	13,750
Current assets		
Inventories	8,234	7,146
Trade and other receivables	6,827	6,954
Cash and cash equivalents	0	135
	15,061	14,235
Total assets	30,411	27,985
EQUITY AND LIABILITIES		
Equity		
Share capital	10,500	10,000
Share premium	1,200	1,000
Retained earnings	8,973	8,363
Total equity	20,673	19,363
Non-current liabilities		
Bank loans	1,800	2,000
	1,800	2,000
Current liabilities		
Trade and other payables	7,102	6,047
Tax liability	350	575
Bank overdraft	486	0
	7,938	6,622
Total liabilities	9,738	8,622
Total equity and liabilities	30,411	27,985

Further information:

- The total depreciation charge for the year was £2,340,000.
- Property, plant and equipment costing £520,000 with accumulated depreciation of £380,000 was sold in the year.
- All sales and purchases were on credit. Other expenses were paid for in cash.
- A dividend of £1,050,000 was paid during the year.

(a) Prepare a reconciliation of profit from operations to net cash from operating activities for Carmen Ltd for the year ended 31 March 20X1.

(b) Prepare the statement of cash flows for Carmen Ltd for the year ended 31 March 20X1.

(c) Draft the statement of changes in equity for Carmen Ltd for the year ended 31 March 20X1.

6.5 Set out below are financial statements for Underdesk Limited for the year ending 20-7 and also for the previous year.

Underdesk Limited: Statement of profit or loss for the year ended 31 December

	20-7	20-6
Continuing operations	£000	£000
Revenue	5,490	4,573
Cost of sales	–3,861	–3,201
Gross profit	1,629	1,372
Depreciation	–672	–445
Other expenses	–313	–297
Gain on disposal of non-current assets	29	13
Profit from operations	673	643
Finance costs	–156	–47
Profit before tax	517	596
Tax	–129	–124
Profit for the year from continuing operations	388	472

Underdesk Limited: Statement of financial position as at 31 December

	20-7	20-6
ASSETS	£000	£000
Non-current assets	5,461	2,979
Current assets		
Inventories	607	543
Trade and other receivables	481	426
Cash and cash equivalents	–	104
	1,088	1,073
Total assets	6,549	4,052
EQUITY AND LIABILITIES		
Equity		
Share capital	1,400	800
Share premium	400	100
Retained earnings	2,460	2,168
Total equity	4,260	3,068
Non-current liabilities		
Bank loans	1,700	520
	1,700	520
Current liabilities		
Trade and other payables	371	340
Tax liability	129	124
Bank overdraft	89	–
	589	464
Total liabilities	2,289	984
Total equity and liabilities	6,549	4,052

Further information:

*   A dividend of £96,000 was paid during the year.

*   Non-current assets costing £187,000 with accumulated depreciation of £102,000 were disposed in 20-7 for £114,000. There were no other disposals in the year.

*   All revenue sales and purchases were on credit. Other expenses were paid for in cash.

Required:

Task 1

Provide a reconciliation of profit from operations to net cash from operating activities for the year ended 31 December 20-7.

Task 2

Prepare the statement of cash flows for Underdesk Limited for the year ended 31 December 20-7 in accordance with the requirements of IAS 7.

7 Interpretation of financial statements

7.1 A limited company has the following statement of profit or loss:

	£000
Continuing operations	
Revenue	225
Cost of sales	−140
Gross profit	85
Distribution costs	−20
Administrative expenses	−25
Profit from operations	40
Finance costs	−10
Profit before tax	30
Tax	−8
Profit for the year from continuing operations	22

(a) State the formula that is used to calculate each of the following ratios:

(1) Gross profit percentage

(2) Distribution costs/revenue percentage

(3) Operating profit percentage

(4) Interest cover

(b) Calculate the above ratios (to the nearest one decimal place)

7.2   The following information is taken from the statement of financial position of a limited company.

	£000
Inventories	380
Trade receivables	450
Cash and cash equivalents	40
Trade payables	410
Non-current liabilities	320
Share capital	450
Retained earnings	140
Further information:	
Revenue for year	4,390
Cost of sales for year	3,360

(a)   State the formula that is used to calculate each of the following ratios:

(1)   Current ratio

(2)   Acid test (quick) ratio

(3)   Inventory turnover

(4)   Inventory holding period

(5)   Trade receivables collection period

(6)   Trade payables payment period

(7)   Gearing

(b)   Calculate the above ratios (to the nearest one decimal place)

7.3   The following information is taken from the financial statements of a limited company.

	£000
Revenue	1,450
Profit from operations	120
Profit after tax	90
Non-current assets	350
Total assets	870
Share capital (£1 ordinary shares)	500
Retained earnings	220
Non-current liabilities	100
Current liabilities	50

(a)   State the formula that is used to calculate each of the following ratios:

    (1)   Return on capital employed

    (2)   Operating profit percentage

    (3)   Return on shareholders' funds

    (4)   Asset turnover (net assets)

    (5)   Asset turnover (non-current assets)

(b)   Calculate the above ratios (to the nearest one decimal place)

7.4 Bragg plc wants to acquire a majority holding in a private limited company. The Managing Director of Bragg plc has asked you to analyse the financial statements of two possible companies and to deal with some queries he has about financial statements. He has asked you to consider the profitability of the companies and their financial position. The financial statements of the two companies are set out below and on the next page.

Summary statements of profit or loss
for the year ended 31 March 20-4

	Roy Limited	Ishiguro Limited
	£000	*£000*
Continuing operations		
Revenue	8,483	10,471
Cost of sales	–3,732	–5,026
Gross profit	4,751	5,445
Distribution costs	–1,218	–1,483
Administrative expenses	–903	–1,658
Profit from operations	2,630	2,304
Finance costs	–160	–520
Profit before tax	2,470	1,784
Tax	–593	–428
Profit for the year from continuing operations	1,877	1,356

Statements of financial position as at 31 March 20-4

	Roy Limited	Ishiguro Limited
ASSETS	*£000*	*£000*
Non-current assets	6,806	12,579
Current assets		
Inventories	2,531	2,181
Trade receivables	1,054	2,309
Cash and cash equivalents	828	5
	4,413	4,495
Total assets	11,219	17,074
EQUITY AND LIABILITIES		
Equity		
Share capital	2,000	2,000
Share premium	1,000	500
Retained earnings	4,367	4,997
Total equity	7,367	7,497
Non-current liabilities		
Bank loans	2,000	6,500
	2,000	6,500
Current liabilities		
Trade payables	1,259	2,166
Bank overdraft	–	483
Tax liability	593	428
	1,852	3,077
Total liabilities	3,852	9,577
Total equity and liabilities	11,219	17,074

Required:

Prepare a report for Bragg plc that includes the following:

(a)   a calculation (to the nearest one decimal place) of the following four ratios of Roy Limited and Ishiguro Limited:

return on shareholders' funds, gross profit percentage, gearing, interest cover

(b)   an explanation of the meaning of each ratio and a comment on the relative profitability and financial position of the two companies based on the ratios calculated

(c)   a conclusion as to which company to invest in, based only on these ratios and your analysis

7.5 The directors of Mercia Printers Ltd, a medium-sized printing firm, have recently read the industry's trade magazine and seen an article quoting the following average ratios for the printing sector:

Return on capital employed	16%
Gearing	21%
Current ratio	1.8:1
Operating profit percentage	8%
Trade payables payment period	62 days

The magazine article discusses the benefits of printing companies benchmarking their own performance against the sector's industrial average in order to assess overall performance and efficiency.

Mercia Printers Limited's statement of profit or loss and statement of financial position are set out below and on the next page.

Mercia Printers Limited

Statement of profit or loss for the year ended 31 August 20-4

	£000
Continuing operations	
Revenue	2,750
Cost of sales	–2,200
Gross profit	550
Distribution costs	–140
Administrative expenses	–210
Profit from operations	200
Finance costs	–63
Profit before tax	137
Tax	–41
Profit for the year from continuing operations	96

Mercia Printers Limited

Statement of financial position as at 31 August 20-4

ASSETS	£000
Non-current assets	450
Current assets	
Inventories	215
Trade receivables	352
Cash and cash equivalents	13
	580
Total assets	1,030
EQUITY AND LIABILITIES	
Equity	
Share capital	240
Retained earnings	366
Total equity	606
Non-current liabilities	250
	250
Current liabilities	
Trade payables	133
Tax liability	41
	174
Total liabilities	424
Total equity and liabilities	1,030

Required:

Write a report for the directors of Mercia Printers Limited, assessing the performance of the company.

The draft report should include:

(a) A calculation (to the nearest one decimal place) from the financial statements of Mercia Printers Limited of the appropriate ratios listed in the magazine article (see above). You should quote the formulas used and show detailed workings for each ratio.

(b) An assessment of the company's overall performance, comparing its ratios with the sector average.

8 Consolidated financial statements

- Blank photocopiable pro-formas in the format used in AAT Assessments – of the consolidated statement of profit or loss, and the consolidated statement of financial position, are included in the Appendix – it is advisable to enlarge them to full A4 size. Blank workings sheets are also included in the Appendix.

- Pro-formas and workings sheets are also available to download from www.osbornebooks.co.uk.

8.1 Wyvern plc invested £260,000 in 150,000 ordinary shares of £1 each in Sidbury Limited. At the date of acquisition the equity of Sidbury Limited comprised £200,000 in share capital and £120,000 in retained earnings.

What is the value of goodwill at the date of acquisition?

	✔
£240,000	
£20,000	
£60,000	
£50,000	

8.2 At 31 March 20X1 the equity of Teme Limited comprises £100,000 in share capital and £80,000 in retained earnings. The parent company, Severn plc, currently owns 60,000 of £1 ordinary shares in Teme Limited.

What is the value of the non-controlling interest at 31 March 20X1?

	✔
£180,000	
£108,000	
£80,000	
£72,000	

8.3   Star plc owns 70% of the ordinary shares in Buck Limited. Revenue for the year ended 31 March 20X1 is: Star £500,000, Buck £140,000. The revenue of Star plc includes goods sold to Buck Limited for £20,000. All of these goods still remain in the inventory of Buck Limited at the end of the year.

What is the value for revenue that will be shown in the consolidated statement of profit or loss for Star plc and its subsidiary undertaking for the year ended 31 March 20X1?

	✔
£640,000	
£661,000	
£620,000	
£626,000	

8.4   IFRS 3, *Business Combinations*, identifies a number of features in the preparation of consolidated financial statements. Explain the following:

- method of accounting to be used in acquisitions
- assets and liabilities acquired
- goodwill

8.5   **(a)**   In business combinations, how are fair values to be treated on acquisition?

   (b)   What effect do fair values have on the calculations for:
- goodwill
- non-controlling interest
- post-acquisition profits

8.6 You have been asked to assist in the preparation of the consolidated financial statements of the Shopan Group. Set out below are the statements of financial position of Shopan Limited and its subsidiary undertaking Hower Limited, as at 30 September 20-9:

Statements of financial position as at 30 September 20-9

	Shopan Limited	Hower Limited
ASSETS	£000	£000
Non-current assets	6,273	1,633
Investment in Hower Limited	2,100	
Current assets		
Inventories	1,901	865
Trade receivables	1,555	547
Cash and cash equivalents	184	104
	3,640	1,516
Total assets	12,013	3,149
EQUITY AND LIABILITIES		
Equity		
Share capital	2,000	500
Share premium	950	120
Retained earnings	4,246	1,484
Total equity	7,196	2,104
Non-current liabilities		
Loan	2,870	400
Current liabilities		
Trade payables	1,516	457
Tax liability	431	188
	1,947	645
Total liabilities	4,817	1,045
Total equity and liabilities	12,013	3,149

Further information:
- The share capital of both Shopan Limited and Hower Limited consists of ordinary shares of £1 each.
- Shopan Limited acquired 375,000 of the issued shares and voting rights in Hower Limited on 30 September 20-9.
- The fair value of the non-current assets of Hower Limited at 30 September 20-9 was £2,033,000.
- Shopan Limited has decided non-controlling interest will be valued at their proportionate share of net assets.

Required:

Task 1
Prepare the consolidated statement of financial position for Shopan Limited and its subsidiary undertaking as at 30 September 20-9.

Task 2
IFRS 10, *Consolidated Financial Statements*, defines power over an investee as 'existing rights that give the current ability to direct the relevant activities'. Give two of the criteria that, according to IFRS 10, give power over an investee.

8.7   The Finance Director of Fairway plc has asked you to prepare the draft consolidated statement of profit or loss for the group. The company has one subsidiary, Green Limited. The statements of comprehensive income of the two companies, prepared for internal purposes, for the year ended 30 June 20-2 are set out below:

Statements of profit or loss for the year ended 30 June 20-2

	Fairway plc	Green Limited
Continuing operations	£000	£000
Revenue	12,200	4,400
Cost of sales	–8,500	–3,100
Gross profit	3,700	1,300
Distribution costs	–1,600	–500
Administrative expenses	–400	–200
Dividends received from Green Limited	80	–
Profit from operations	1,780	600
Finance costs	–300	–200
Profit before tax	1,480	400
Tax	–400	–100
Profit for the year from continuing operations	1,080	300

Further information:

- Fairway plc acquired 80% of the issued share capital and voting rights of Green Limited on 1 July 20-1.

- During the year Green Limited sold goods which had cost £750,000 to Fairway plc for £1,000,000. All the goods had been sold by Fairway plc by the end of the year.

- Dividends paid during the year were:
    - Fairway plc, £700,000
    - Green Limited, £100,000

- There were no impairment losses on goodwill during the year.

Required:

Draft a consolidated statement of profit or loss for Fairway plc and its subsidiary undertaking for the year ended 30 June 20-2.

8.8 Perran Plc acquired 80% of the issued share capital and voting rights of Porth Ltd on 1 April 20X0 for £750,000. At that date Porth Ltd had issued share capital of £600,000 and retained earnings of £240,000.

Extracts from the statements of financial position for the two companies one year later at 31 March 20X1 are as follows:

	Perran Plc	Porth Ltd
	£000	£000
Assets		
Investment in Porth Ltd	750	
Non-current assets	770	800
Current assets	450	350
Total assets	1,970	1,150
Equity and liabilities		
Equity		
Share capital	1,000	600
Retained earnings	450	300
Total equity	1,450	900
Non-current liabilities	120	50
Current liabilities	400	200
Total liabilities	520	250
Total equity and liabilities	1,970	1,150

Further information:

- Included within the current assets of Perran Plc and in the current liabilities of Porth Ltd is an inter-company transaction for £70,000 that took place in early March 20X1.
- Perran Plc has decided non-controlling interest will be valued at their proportionate share of net assets.

(a) **Draft the consolidated statement of financial position for Perran Plc and its subsidiary undertaking as at 31 March 20X1.**

(Activity continues on next page.)

Fistral Plc acquired 75% of the issued share capital and voting rights of Beach Ltd on 1 April 20X0.

Extracts from their statements of profit or loss for the year ended 31 March 20X1 are shown below:

	Fistral Plc	Beach Ltd
	£000	£000
Continuing operations		
Revenue	18,250	6,450
Cost of sales	−11,800	−3,100
Gross profit	6,450	3,350
Other income – dividend from Beach Ltd	400	–
Distribution costs and administrative expenses	−3,750	−1,650
Profit before tax	3,100	1,700

Additional data:

During the year Beach Ltd sold goods which had cost £50,000 to Fistral Plc for £90,000. Half of these goods still remain in inventory at the end of the year.

(b) Draft the consolidated statement of profit or loss for Fistral Plc and its subsidiary undertaking up to and including the profit before tax line for the year ended 31 March 20X1.

Chapter activities answers

1 Purpose of financial statements

1.1 **(a)** According to the *Conceptual Framework for Financial Reporting* the objective of financial reporting is:

- to provide financial information about the reporting entity
- that is useful to existing and potential investors, lenders and other payables/creditors
- in making decisions about providing resources to the entity

(b)

User	Purpose
Existing and potential investors	To enable them to assess how effectively management has fulfilled its stewardship role and to consider information that is useful in taking decisions about their existing investment or potential investment in the entity
Lenders	To assess whether loans will be repaid and related interest will be repaid when due/to help potential lenders decide whether to lend and on what terms
Other payables/creditors	To decide whether to sell to the entity and to assess the likelihood that amounts owing will be paid when due

1.2   income – expenses = profits or losses

1.3   £35,250 – £14,600 = £20,650

1.4

Statement	Characteristic
Financial information that is available to decision-makers in time to be capable in influencing their decisions	Timeliness
Financial information that helps assure users that information is faithfully represented	Verifiability
Users of financial statements are able to identify and understand similarities in, and differences among, items	Comparability
Users of financial statements are presented with information that is classified and characterised clearly and concisely	Understandability

1.5   **(a)**   The accounting equation is:

Assets – Liabilities = Equity

The elements are defined as follows:

- assets – resources controlled by the entity as a result of past events and from which future economic benefits are expected to flow to the entity

- liabilities – present obligations of the entity arising from past events, the settlement of which is expected to result in an outflow from the entity of resources embodying economic benefits

- equity – the residual interest in the assets of the entity after deducting all its liabilities

(b)   •   profit for the year increases the equity in the accounting equation

- this is matched by an increase in the assets of the business that amount to the difference between assets minus liabilities

1.6   **(a)**   The elements that appear in financial statements according to the *Conceptual Framework for Financial Reporting* are:

- assets
- liabilities
- equity
- income
- expenses

(b)   The elements that appear in the statement of profit or loss and other comprehensive income are:

- income
- expenses

Income is increases in economic benefits during the accounting period in the form of inflows or enhancements of assets, or decreases of liabilities that result in increases in equity, other than those relating to contributions from equity participants.

Expenses are decreases in economic benefits during the accounting period in the form of outflows or depletions of assets or incurring of liabilities that result in decreases in equity, other than those relating to distributions to equity participants.

2 Introduction to limited company financial statements

2.1 **(a)** **Public limited company (plc)**

A company may become a public limited company if it has:

- issued share capital of over £50,000

- at least two members (shareholders) and at least two directors

A public limited company may raise capital from the public on the Stock Exchange or similar markets, but not all do so.

(b) **Private limited company (ltd)**

A private limited company is defined by the Companies Act 2006 as 'any company that is not a public company'.

A private limited company has:

- no minimum requirement for issued share capital

- at least one member (shareholder) and at least one director who may be the sole shareholder

The shares of a private limited company are not traded publicly on the Stock Exchange or similar markets, but are transferable between individuals.

2.2 anyone taking legal action proceeds against the company and not the individual shareholders

2.3 ordinary shares

2.4 £55,000

2.5 **Crantock plc – Statement of profit or loss for the year ending 31 March 20-2**

Continuing operations	£000	£000
Revenue		2,295
Opening inventories	160	
Purchases	1,200	
Closing inventories	180	
Cost of sales		−1,180
Gross profit		1,115
Overheads:		
Administrative expenses		−240
Distribution costs		−500
Profit before tax		375
Tax		−65
Profit for the year from continuing operations		310

Crantock plc – Statement of financial position as at 31 March 20-2

	Cost	Dep'n	Net
ASSETS	*£000*	*£000*	*£000*
Non-current assets			
Plant and equipment	1,600	500	1,100
Current assets			
Inventories			180
Trade and other receivables			525
Cash and cash equivalents			75
			780
Total assets			1,880
EQUITY AND LIABILITIES			
Equity			
Share capital			700
Share premium			200
Retained earnings			520
Total equity			1,420
Current liabilities			
Trade and other payables			395
Tax liability			65
Total liabilities			460
Total equity and liabilities			1,880

Tutorial note *(£000)*:

Retained earnings

Trial balance	350
Profit for the year	310
Dividends paid	−140
	520

2.6 **Playfair Ltd – Statement of profit or loss for the year ending 31 December 20-3**

Continuing operations	£000	£000
Revenue		2,340
Opening inventories	250	
Purchases	1,650	
Closing inventories	−280	
Cost of sales		−1,620
Gross profit		720
Overheads:		
Administrative expenses		−210
Distribution costs		−320
Profit from operations		190
Finance costs		−40
Profit before tax		150
Tax		−30
Profit for the year from continuing operations		120

Playfair Ltd – Statement of financial position as at 31 December 20-3

	Cost	Dep'n	Net
ASSETS	*£000*	*£000*	*£000*
Non-current assets			
Land	500	–	500
Plant and equipment	800	390	410
	1,300	390	910
Current assets			
Inventories			280
Trade and other receivables			350
Cash and cash equivalents			140
			770
Total assets			1,680
EQUITY AND LIABILITIES			
Equity			
Share capital			580
Share premium			50
Retained earnings			610
Total equity			1,240
Non-current liabilities			
Bank loans			200
			200
Current liabilities			
Trade and other payables			210
Tax liability			30
			240
Total liabilities			440
Total equity and liabilities			1,680

Tutorial note *(£000)*:

Depreciation of plant and equipment

Plant and equipment at cost	800
20% depreciation	160
Allocated to	
Distribution costs	80
Administrative expenses	80
	160

Accumulated depreciation

230 + 160	=	390

Administrative expenses

Trial balance	110
Depreciation of plant and equipment	80
Increase in allowance for doubtful debts	20
	210

Distribution costs

Trial balance	240
Depreciation of plant and equipment	80
	320

Finance costs

Trial balance	20
Interest accrued	20
	40

Trade and other receivables

Trial balance	350
Prepayments	40
Allowance for doubtful debts	−40
	350

Retained earnings

Trial balance	540
Profit for the year	120
Dividends paid	−50
	610

Trade and other payables

Trial balance	160
Accruals	30
Interest accrued	20
	210

3 Published financial statements of limited companies

3.1 'The objective of financial statements is to provide **information** about the **financial** position, financial **performance** and **cash** flows of an entity that is **useful** to a wide range of **users** in making **economic** decisions.'

3.2 1. statement of profit or loss and other comprehensive income;

2. statement of cash flows;

4. statement of changes in equity

3.3 (1) nine months (2) six months

3.4 1. revaluation reserve; 3. share premium

3.5 1. a rights issue of shares

3.6 **(a)** Wymark Ltd – Statement of profit or loss and other comprehensive income for the year ended 31 March 20X4

	£000
Revenue	10,884
Cost of sales	−7,655
Gross profit	3,229
Distribution costs	−1,100
Administrative expenses	−544
Profit from operations	1,585
Finance costs	−200
Profit before tax	1,385
Tax	−348
Profit for the year from continuing operations	1,037
Other comprehensive income for the year	500
Total comprehensive income for the year	1,537

Workings

Cost of sales	£000
Opening inventories	2,043
Purchases	7,854
Closing inventories	−2,422
Depreciation	*180
Cost of sales =	7,655

* depreciation: buildings £1,500 x 2% x 50% = £15; plant and equipment (£2,722 – £1,402) x 25% x 50% = £165; total £180

Distribution costs	£000
Distribution costs	980
Accrual	12
Depreciation	*108
Distribution costs =	1,100

* depreciation as per cost of sales, but at 30%

Administrative expenses	£000
Administrative expenses	461
Bad (irrecoverable) debt	11
Depreciation	*72
Administrative expenses =	544

* depreciation as per cost of sales, but at 20%

(b) **Wymark Ltd – Statement of changes in equity for the year ended 31 March 20X4**

	Share capital	Other reserves	Retained earnings	Total equity
	£000	£000	£000	£000
Balance at 1 April 20X3	3,500		1,457	4,957
Changes in equity for 20X4				
Total comprehensive income		500	1,037	1,537
Dividends			−600	−600
Issue of share capital				
Balance at 31 March 20X4	3,500	500	1,894	5,894

(c) **Wymark Ltd – Statement of financial position as at 31 March 20X4**

	£000
Assets	
Non-current assets	
Property, plant and equipment	5,758
Current assets	
Inventories	2,422
Trade and other receivables	1,833
Cash and cash equivalents	155
	4,410
Total assets	10,168
EQUITY AND LIABILITIES	
Equity	
Share capital	3,500
Retained earnings	1,894
Revaluation reserve	500
Total equity	5,894
Non-current liabilities	
Bank loan	2,500
	2,500
Current liabilities	
Trade and other payables	1,426
Tax liability	348
	1,774
Total liabilities	4,274
Total equity and liabilities	10,168

Workings

Property, plant and equipment	£000
Land and buildings – value	5,500
Accumulated depreciation – land and buildings	*–732
Plant and equipment – cost	2,722
Accumulated depreciation – plant and equipment	**–1,732
Property, plant and equipment =	5,758

* £702 + £30
** £1,402 + £330

Trade and other receivables	£000
Trade and other receivables	1,802
Bad (irrecoverable) debt	–11
Prepayments – trial balance	42
Trade and other receivables =	1,833

Trade and other payables	£000
Trade and other payables	1,309
Accruals – trial balance	105
Additional distribution costs accrued	12
Trade and other payables =	1,426

3.7 **(a)** **Nathan Ltd – Statement of profit or loss and other comprehensive income for the year ended 31 March 20X1**

	£000
Revenue	21,495
Cost of sales	−9,331
Gross profit	12,164
Distribution costs	−6,259
Administrative expenses	−4,577
Profit from operations	1,328
Finance costs	−150
Profit before tax	1,178
Tax	−207
Profit for the year from continuing operations	971
Other comprehensive income for the year	0
Total comprehensive income for the year	971

Workings

Cost of sales	£000
Opening inventories	641
Purchases	9,364
Returns outwards	−47
Closing inventories	−627
Cost of sales =	9,331

Distribution costs	£000
Distribution costs	3,852
Accrual	22
Depreciation	*2,385
Distribution costs =	6,259

* depreciation: plant and equipment (£20,500 − £4,600) x 25% x 60% = £2,385

Administrative expenses	£000
Administrative expenses	2,975
Bad (irrecoverable) debt	12
Depreciation	*1,590
Administrative expenses =	4,577

* depreciation as per distribution costs, but at 40%

(b) **Nathan Ltd – Statement of changes in equity for the year ended 31 March 20X1**

	Share capital	Other reserves	Retained earnings	Total equity
	£000	£000	£000	£000
Balance at 1 April 20X0	6,000	1,000	2,537	9,537
Changes in equity for 20X1				
Total comprehensive income			971	971
Dividends			–450	–450
Balance at 31 March 20X1	6,000	1,000	3,058	10,058

(c) **Nathan Ltd – Statement of financial position as at 31 March 20X1**

	£000
Assets	
Non-current assets	
Property, plant and equipment	11,925
Current assets	
Inventories	627
Trade and other receivables	1,720
Cash and cash equivalents	110
	2,457
Total assets	14,382
EQUITY AND LIABILITIES	
Equity	
Share capital	6,000
Retained earnings	3,058
Share premium	1,000
Total equity	10,058
Non-current liabilities	
Bank loan	3,000
	3,000
Current liabilities	
Trade and other payables	1,117
Tax liability	207
	1,324
Total liabilities	4,324
Total equity and liabilities	14,382

Workings

Property, plant and equipment	£000
	0
	0
Plant and equipment – cost	20,500
Accumulated depreciation – plant and equipment	*–8,575
Property, plant and equipment =	11,925

* £4,600 + £3,975

Trade and other receivables	£000
Trade and other receivables	1,546
Bad (irrecoverable) debt	–12
Prepayments – trial balance	186
Trade and other receivables =	1,720

Trade and other payables	£000
Trade and other payables	1,010
Accruals – trial balance	85
Additional distribution costs accrued	22
Trade and other payables =	1,117

4 Accounting for assets

4.1 Task 1

Two criteria for recognition of an item of PPE:

* it is probable that **future economic benefits** will flow to the entity
* the cost of the asset can be **measured reliably**

Task 2

(a) Cost is the purchase price of the asset, including any import duties, plus any costs directly attributable to bring the asset to the location and condition for its intended use, plus the estimated costs of dismantling and removing the asset at the end of its useful life.

(b) **Attributable costs which can be included in the cost of an asset**

Two from:

* costs of site preparation
* initial delivery and handling costs
* installation and assembly costs
* costs of testing the asset
* professional fees, eg engineers, architects

(c) **Costs which cannot be included in the cost of an asset**

Two from:

* administration and other general overhead costs
* start-up costs of a new business or section of the business
* start-up costs for introducing a new product or service – such as advertising and promotional costs

(d) Two models to choose from:

* **Cost model** – the asset is carried at cost less accumulated depreciation and impairment losses
* **Revaluation model** – the asset is carried at a revalued amount, being its fair value less any subsequent depreciation and impairment losses; revaluations are to be made regularly to ensure that the carrying amount does not differ materially from its fair value at the date of the statement of financial position.

4.2 **(a)** IAS 16, *Property, Plant and Equipment*, defines depreciation as the systematic allocation of the depreciable amount of an asset over its useful life. (Depreciable amount is the cost or valuation of the asset, less any residual value.)

(b) • IAS 16 states that, initially, PPE are to be measured at cost in the statement of financial position.

• After acquisition of PPE an entity must choose either the cost model or the revaluation model as its accounting policy – which is then applied to an entire class of PPE.

• Using the cost model, assets are carried in the statement of financial position at cost less accumulated depreciation and impairment losses.

• Using the revaluation model, assets are carried at a revalued amount, being fair value less any subsequent depreciation and impairment losses; revaluations are to be made regularly to ensure that the carrying amounts do not differ materially from fair values at the date of the statement of financial position.

• The residual value and the useful life of an asset are to be reviewed at least annually.

• Depreciation continues to be recognised even if the fair value of an asset exceeds its carrying amount (but there is no need for depreciation when the residual value is greater than the carrying amount).

• Spending money on repair and maintenance of an asset does not remove the need for depreciation.

• When calculating depreciable amount, the residual values of assets are often low or immaterial – for example, the scrap value of a machine is often negligible.

• Depreciation can be applied to separate parts of an asset where each part is a significant cost – for example, the engines of an aircraft are often depreciated separately from the body of the aircraft.

• Depreciation for the period is recognised in the statement of profit or loss and other comprehensive income (unless it is included in the carrying amount of another asset).

• When determining the useful life of an asset, the following factors need to be considered (even if the asset is not being used):

  - expected usage of the asset, ie the expected capacity or output

  - expected physical wear and tear, which depends on operational factors and the repair and maintenance programme

  - technical or commercial obsolescence, eg the introduction of new technology, changes in demand for the product or service

  - legal or similar limits on the use of the asset, eg the period for which an asset is leased

4.3 The entity has no specific aim or application for the intangible asset

4.4 Reliability

4.5 **(a)** IAS 38, *Intangible Assets*, defines an intangible asset as

- an identifiable non-monetary asset

- without physical substance

(b) Before an intangible asset arising from development is recognised as an intangible asset in the financial statements of Tanhosier Ltd they would have to demonstrate:

- the technical feasibility of completing the intangible asset so that it will be available for use or sale

- the intention to complete the intangible asset and to use or sell it

- its ability to use or sell the intangible asset

- the way in which the intangible asset will generate probable future economic benefits

- the availability of resources to complete the development and to use or sell the intangible asset

- its ability to measure reliably the expenditure attributable to the intangible asset

4.6 1. land and buildings; 3. goodwill; 4. vehicles

Note that IAS 36 does not apply to current assets, such as inventories.

4.7   **Task 1**

External indicators

Two from:

- a significant fall in the asset's market value

- adverse effects on the entity caused by technology, markets, the economy, laws

- increases in interest rates

- the stock market value of the entity is less than the carrying amount of net assets

Internal indicators

Two from:

- obsolescence or physical damage to the asset

- adverse effects on the asset of a significant reorganisation within the entity

- the economic performance of the asset is worse than expected

Note: Other indicators – such as evidence from internal financial statements – can indicate that an asset may be impaired.

Examples include:

- a fall in the profit (or an increase in the loss) from operations

- a fall in the cash flows from operations, or a negative cash flow

- a fall in budgeted cash flows, or budgeted profit from operations

Task 2

(a)   An impairment review involves comparing the asset's carrying amount with the recoverable amount.

(b)   An impairment review is carried out in three steps:

Step 1   Identify the asset's carrying amount (ie cost/revaluation less depreciation/amortisation to date)

Step 2   Identify the asset's recoverable amount, ie the higher of fair value less costs of disposal (the net realisable value of the asset) and value in use (the present value of the future cash flows expected to be derived from the asset, including cash from its ultimate disposal).

Step 3   If carrying amount is greater than recoverable amount, then the asset is impaired and should be written down to its recoverable amount in the statement of financial position. The amount of the impairment loss is recognised as an expense in the statement of profit or loss and other comprehensive income unless it relates to a previously revalued asset, when it is recognised as a decrease in other comprehensive income and is debited to the revaluation surplus within equity (to the extent of the revaluation surplus for that particular asset).

4.8   1 and 3

4.9

Year	Finance charge
	£
20-1	1,500
20-2	1,200
20-3	900
20-4	600
20-5	300

4.10   **(a)**   The two inventory valuation methods allowed by IAS 2, *Inventories*, are:

- FIFO (first in, first out) assumes that those items bought first are the first to be used in production or selling.

- AVCO (average cost), or weighted average cost method whereby the average cost of items held at the beginning of any period is calculated and, as the inventories are issued for production or selling purposes, all items are issued at that average price. When new inventory is received, the average issue price will then need to be recalculated.

(b)   LIFO (last in, first out) cannot be used under IAS 2.

4.11   At the lower of cost and net realisable value

4.12   IAS 38, *Intangible Assets*, sets out the accounting treatment for expenditure on research and development.

The costs of developing the new lawnmower are likely to be classified, for the purpose of the financial statements, as development costs. Such costs are either recognised as an expense in the statement of profit or loss and other comprehensive income when they are incurred, or they may be capitalised (ie recognised on the statement of financial position) as an intangible asset. In order to apply the latter treatment, Lawnderer Limited must be able to demonstrate all of the following criteria given by IAS 38:

- the technical feasibility of completing the intangible asset so that it will be available for use or sale

- its intention to complete the intangible asset and to use or sell it

- its ability to use or sell the intangible asset

- the way in which the intangible asset will generate probable future economic benefits

- the availability of resources to complete the development and to use or sell the intangible asset

- its ability to measure the development expenditure reliably

The project would appear to fulfil all of the criteria, subject to the resource of finance being available either from the company's bank or from shareholders willing to invest more capital.

If all of the criteria are met then the costs of the development may be capitalised and carried on the statement of financial position as an intangible asset until such time as the project commences commercial production. The intangible asset will then be amortised over its useful life against future profits. The effect of this is that the development costs will not affect profits until production commences and sales are made.

5 Accounting for liabilities and the statement of profit or loss

5.1   In the statement of profit or loss and other comprehensive income and as a current liability in the statement of financial position

5.2   At the lower of the fair value of the asset being leased and the present value of the minimum lease payments

5.3   **(a)**   • A **provision** is a liability of uncertain timing or amount

   • A **contingent liability** is

   - either a possible obligation arising from past events whose existence will be confirmed only by the occurrence or non-occurrence of one or more uncertain future events not wholly within the entity's control

   - or a present obligation that arises from past events but is not recognised because:

      (1)   either it is not probable that an outflow of economic benefits will be required to settle the obligation

      (2)   or the obligation cannot be measured with sufficient reliability

   • A **contingent asset** is a possible asset arising from past events whose existence will be confirmed only by the occurrence or non-occurrence of one or more uncertain future events not wholly within the entity's control.

   (b)   • A **provision** is to be recognised as a liability in the financial statements when:

   - an entity has a present obligation as a result of a past event

   - it is probable that an outflow of economic benefits will be required to settle the obligation

   - a reliable estimate can be made of the amount of the obligation

   Note that the word 'probable' used in IAS 37 means that there is a more than 50% likelihood of occurrence of the obligation.

   A provision should also be disclosed as a note to the financial statements, giving:

   - details of changes in the amount of provisions between the beginning and end of the year

   - a description of the provision(s) and expected timings of any resulting transfers

   - an indication of the uncertainties regarding the amount or timing of any resulting transfers

A **contingent liability** is not recognised in the financial statements; however, it should be disclosed as a note to the financial statements which includes:

- a brief description of the nature of the contingent liability

- an estimate of its financial effect

- an indication of the uncertainties relating to the amount or timing of any outflow

- the possibility of any reimbursement

Note that a contingent liability is a 'possible' obligation, ie a less than 50% likelihood of its occurrence.

Where a contingent liability is considered to be remote, then no disclosure is required in the notes to the financial statements.

A **contingent asset** is not recognised in the financial statements. It is disclosed only where an inflow of economic benefits is probable; disclosure in the notes to the financial statements should include:

- a brief description of the nature of the contingent asset

- an estimate of its financial effect

5.4   2 only

5.5   True

5.6   **Notes for the directors of Cortez Limited**

(a)   The fire at the warehouse and the subsequent losses that resulted are a non-adjusting event under IAS 10, *Events after the Reporting Period*. These are events that take place after the financial statements have been prepared at the year end and before the time when the statements are authorised for issue to interested parties. Provision is required in the year end accounts only for adjusting events which are events that provide evidence of conditions that existed at the end of the reporting period. Non-adjusting events should be disclosed if they are of such materiality that non-disclosure would affect the ability of the users of financial statements to reach a proper understanding of the financial position of the company. As this event is disclosed in a note to the accounts it meets these criteria.

(b)   The company will have entered into a lease for non-current assets, such as machinery or vehicles. Cortez Ltd is the lessee and the lessor will, most likely, be a finance company.

As it is a finance lease, it is a longer term lease, under which substantially all of the risks and rewards of ownership are transferred to the lessee.

The non-current liability is the amount of the finance lease – shown at the lower of the fair value of the asset being leased and the present value of the minimum lease payments. There may also be a current liability showing on the statement of financial position for the amount of the finance lease payments due within the next 12 months.

The non-current assets section of the statement of financial position will indicate the asset(s) being leased.

5.7   **(a)**   IAS 18, *Revenue*, defines revenue as the gross inflow of economic benefits during the period arising in the course of the ordinary activities of an entity when those inflows result in increases in equity, other than increases relating to contributions from equity participants.

As well as the sale of goods, other examples of revenue are rendering of services, interest, royalties and dividends.

(b)   Revenue is to be measured at the fair value of the consideration received or receivable.

Fair value is the price that would be received to sell an asset or paid to transfer a liability in an orderly transaction between market participants at the measurement date.

(c)   Revenue from the sale of goods should be recognised when all of the following criteria have been met:

- the seller of the goods has transferred to the buyer the significant risks and rewards of ownership

- the seller retains no continuing managerial involvement in the goods and no effective control over the goods

- the amount of revenue can be measured reliably

- it is probable that the economic benefits will flow to the seller

- the costs incurred, or to be incurred, in respect of the transaction can be measured reliably

6   Statement of cash flows

6.1   £45,000 inflow

6.2   £6,000 outflow

6.3   1 – 2 – 3 – 4, ie cash received from sales, minus cash paid to suppliers and employees, minus interest paid, minus tax paid.

6.4 **(a)**

Carmen Ltd – Reconciliation of profit from operations to net cash from operating activities	
	£000
Profit from operations	2,200
Adjustments for:	
Depreciation	2,340
Dividends received	–30
Loss on disposal of property, plant and equipment	50
Decrease/increase in inventories	–1,088
Decrease/increase in trade and other receivables	127
Decrease/increase in trade and other payables	1,055
Cash generated by operations	4,654
Tax paid	–575
Interest paid	–190
Net cash from operating activities	3,889

(b)

Carmen Ltd – Statement of cash flows for year ended 31 March 20X1	
	£000
Net cash from operating activities	3,889
Investing activities	
Dividends received	30
Proceeds on disposal of property, plant and equipment	90
Purchases of property, plant and equipment	–4,080
Net cash used in investing activities	–3,960
Financing activities	
Bank loans repaid	–200
Proceeds of share issue	700
Dividends paid	–1,050
Net cash used in financing activities	–550
Net increase/decrease in cash and cash equivalents	–621
Cash and cash equivalents at beginning of year	135
Cash and cash equivalents at end of year	–486

(c)

Carmen Ltd – Statement of changes in equity for the year ended 31 March 20X1

	Share Capital £000	Other Reserves £000	Retained Earnings £000	Total Equity £000
Balance at 1 April 20X0	10,000	1,000	8,363	19,363
Changes in equity for 20X1				
Profit for the year			1,660	1,660
Dividends			–1,050	–1,050
Issue of share capital	500	200		700
Balance at 31 March 20X1	10,500	1,200	8,973	20,673

Workings:

Proceeds on disposal of PPE	£000
Carrying amount of PPE sold	*140
Loss on disposal	–50
Proceeds on disposal of PPE =	90

* cost price 520, accumulated depreciation –380 = carrying amount 140

Purchase of PPE	£000
PPE at start of year	13,750
Depreciation charge	–2,340
Carrying amount of PPE sold	–140
PPE at end of year	–15,350
Total PPE additions =	–4,080*

*outflow of cash

Dividends received

In AAT Assessments, dividends received are classed as investing activities. Note that IAS 7, *Statement of Cash Flows*, does permit dividends (and also interest) to be classified as operating or investing or financing activities – how they are classified should be applied consistently in a company's financial statements.

6.5 Task 1

UNDERDESK LIMITED

Reconciliation of profit from operations to net cash from operating activities for the year ended 31 December 20-7

	£000
Profit from operations	673
Adjustments for:	
Depreciation	672
Gain on disposal of non-current assets	−29
Increase in inventories (607−543)	−64
Increase in trade receivables (481−426)	−55
Increase in trade payables (371−340)	31
Cash generated by operations	1,228
Interest paid	−156
Tax paid	−124
Net cash from operating activities	948

Task 2

UNDERDESK LIMITED

STATEMENT OF CASH FLOWS FOR THE YEAR ENDED 31 DECEMBER 20-7

	£000	£000
Net cash from operating activities		948
Investing activities		
Purchase of non-current assets (see below)	−3,239	
Proceeds on disposal of non-current assets	114	
Net cash used in investing activities		−3,125
Financing activities		
Proceeds of share issue (at a premium)	900	
Repayment of share capital	−	
New bank loans	1,180	
Dividends paid	−96	
Net cash from financing activities		1,984
Net decrease in cash and cash equivalents		−193
Cash and cash equivalents at beginning of year		104
Cash and cash equivalents at end of year		−89

Working note

Purchase of non-current assets *(000)*:

Non-current assets at start of year 2,979, depreciation charge −672, carrying amount on non-current assets sold −85, non-current assets at end of year −5,461, total non-current asset additions = −3,239 (outflow of cash)

7 Interpretation of financial statements

7.1

Ratio	(a) Formula	(b) Calculation of ratio (amounts in £000)
(1) Gross profit percentage	$\dfrac{\text{Gross profit}}{\text{Revenue}} \times 100$	$\dfrac{85}{225} \times 100 = 37.8\%$
(2) Distribution costs/revenue percentage	$\dfrac{\text{Distribution costs} \times 100}{\text{Revenue}}$	$\dfrac{20}{225} \times 100 = 8.9\%$
(3) Operating profit percentage	$\dfrac{\text{Profit from operations} \times 100}{\text{Revenue}}$	$\dfrac{40}{225} \times 100 = 17.8\%$
(4) Interest cover	$\dfrac{\text{Profit from operations}}{\text{Finance costs}}$	$\dfrac{40}{10} = 4 \text{ times}$

7.2

Ratio	(a) Formula	(b) Calculation of ratio (amounts in £000)
(1) Current ratio	$\dfrac{\text{Current assets}}{\text{Current liabilities}}$	$\dfrac{870}{410}$ $=$ 2.1:1
(2) Acid test (quick) ratio	$\dfrac{\text{Current assets} - \text{inventories}}{\text{Current liabilities}}$	$\dfrac{870 - 380}{410}$ $=$ 1.2:1
(3) Inventory turnover	$\dfrac{\text{Cost of sales}}{\text{Inventories}}$	$\dfrac{3,360}{380}$ $=$ 8.8 times
(4) Inventory holding period	$\dfrac{\text{Inventories}}{\text{Cost of sales}}$ x 365 days	$\dfrac{380}{3,360}$ x 365 = 41.3 days
(5) Trade receivables collection period	$\dfrac{\text{Trade receivables}}{\text{Revenue}}$ x 365 days	$\dfrac{450}{4,390}$ x 365 = 37.4 days
(6) Trade payables payment period	$\dfrac{\text{Trade payables}}{\text{Cost of sales}}$ x 365 days	$\dfrac{410}{3,360}$ x 365 = 44.5 days
(7) Gearing	$\dfrac{\text{Non-current liabilities}}{\text{Total equity} + \text{Non-current liabilities}}$ x 100	$\dfrac{320}{590 + 320}$ x 100 = 35.2%

7.3

Ratio	(a) Formula	(b) Calculation of ratio (amounts in £000)
(1) Return on capital employed	$\dfrac{\text{Profit from operations}}{\text{Total equity + Non-current liabilities}} \times 100$	$\dfrac{120}{720 + 100} \times 100 = \quad 14.6\%$
(2) Operating profit percentage	$\dfrac{\text{Profit from operations}}{\text{Revenue}} \times 100$	$\dfrac{120 \times 100}{1,450} \quad = \quad 8.3\%$
(3) Return on share-holders' funds	$\dfrac{\text{Profit after tax}}{\text{Total equity}} \times 100$	$\dfrac{90 \times 100}{720} \quad = \quad 12.5\%$
(4) Asset turnover (net assets)	$\dfrac{\text{Revenue}}{\text{Total assets} - \text{current liabilities}}$	$\dfrac{1,450}{870 - 50} \quad = 1.8 \text{ times}$
(5) Asset turnover (non-current assets)	$\dfrac{\text{Revenue}}{\text{Non-current assets}}$	$\dfrac{1,450}{350} \quad = 4.1 \text{ times}$

7.4

REPORT

To: Managing Director, Bragg Plc   From: AAT student

Subject: Interpretation of ratios   Date: Today

Introduction

This report has been prepared to assist in the interpretation of the financial statements of Roy Limited and Ishiguro Limited, the possible private limited companies in which you are considering the purchase of a majority holding. The report considers the profitability and the financial position of each of the companies for the year ended 31 March 20-4, and compares the results between them.

Calculation of the ratios (amounts in £000)

Ratio	Roy Limited		Ishiguro Limited	
Return on shareholder's funds	$\dfrac{1,877}{7,367}$	= 25.5%	$\dfrac{1,356}{7,497}$	= 18.1%
Gross profit percentage	$\dfrac{4,751}{8,483}$	= 56.0%	$\dfrac{5,445}{10,471}$	= 52.0%
Gearing	$\dfrac{2,000}{7,367 + 2,000}$	= 21.4%	$\dfrac{6,500}{7,497 + 6,500}$	= 46.4%
Interest cover	$\dfrac{2,630}{160}$	= 16.4 times	$\dfrac{2,304}{520}$	= 4.4 times

Explanation and comment

Return on shareholders' funds:

- this ratio measures the percentage of profit after tax available for shareholders that is generated by the use of equity finance
- the return on shareholders' funds of Roy Limited is higher than that of Ishiguro Limited
- this means that more profits for shareholders are generated from an investment in Roy Limited
- thus an investment in Roy Limited is initially more attractive

Gross profit percentage:

- this ratio shows in percentage terms how much gross profit is being generated by the revenue of the company
- the gross profit percentage of Roy Limited is higher than that of Ishiguro Limited
- this indicates that the underlying business in Roy Limited is more profitable than that in Ishiguro Limited
- thus Roy Limited is relatively more attractive than Ishiguro Limited

Gearing:

- gearing measures the percentage of non-current liabilities to total equity and non-current liabilities
- the gearing percentage in Ishiguro Limited is higher than that in Roy Limited
- this indicates that Ishiguro Limited is more reliant on debt than is Roy Limited; Ishiguro Limited is a riskier company to invest in than Roy Limited; there is the risk that Ishiguro may not generate sufficient profits to maintain the dividend to ordinary shareholders; it may fail to meet interest payments from profits if there is a downturn in profitability
- the greater risk to ordinary shareholders makes Ishiguro Limited a relatively less attractive investment

Interest cover:

- this ratio shows how many times the company could meet its finance costs out of profit from operations
- Ishiguro Limited has lower interest cover than Roy Limited
- this means that Ishiguro Limited may have more difficulty than Roy Limited in meeting finance costs out of profits; however, there is still a reasonable margin for comfort as Ishiguro can meet the finance costs four times over at the current level of profits
- nevertheless, Roy Limited is still a more attractive investment as the risk of defaulting on finance costs is very low

Conclusion

- The ratios show that Roy Limited is a relatively more attractive investment than Ishiguro Limited
- Roy Limited is the more profitable company with a higher return on shareholders' funds and higher gross profit percentage
- Roy Limited has a more secure financial position – being lower geared with a much higher interest cover than Ishiguro Limited; this suggests that returns to shareholders from investing in Roy Limited are less risky than those of Ishiguro Limited
- My overall recommendation, on the basis of the ratios calculated and analysis performed, is that Bragg Limited should invest in Roy Limited rather than in Ishiguro Limited

7.5 **(a)** **Mercia Printers Limited**
(amounts in £000)

		Industry average

Return on capital employed

$$\frac{\text{Profit from operations}}{\text{Total equity + Non-current liabilities}} \times 100 \qquad \frac{200}{606 + 250} \times 100 = 23.4\% \qquad 16\%$$

Gearing

$$\frac{\text{Non-current liabilities}}{\text{Total equity + Non-current liabilities}} \times 100 \qquad \frac{250}{606 + 250} \times 100 = 29.2\% \qquad 21\%$$

Current ratio

$$\frac{\text{Current assets}}{\text{Current liabilities}} \qquad \frac{580}{174} \times 100 = 3.3:1 \qquad 1.8:1$$

Operating profit percentage

$$\frac{\text{Profit from operations}}{\text{Revenue}} \times 100 \qquad \frac{200}{2,750} \times 100 = 7.3\% \qquad 8\%$$

Trade payables payment period

$$\frac{\text{Trade payables}}{\text{Cost of sales}} \times 365 \qquad \frac{133}{2,200} \times 365 = 22.1 \text{ days} \qquad 62 \text{ days}$$

(b)

To.   The Directors

From AAT student

Date   Today

Report on Mercia Printers Limited performance and efficiency for the year ended 31 August 20-4

The company has appeared to utilise its capital far more profitably than its competitors. Its **return on capital employed** of 23.4% is much better than the industry average of 16%. Therefore, from a profit and investment point of view, the company is very favourably placed.

Gearing is a measure of risk – it reflects the balance between non-current liabilities and total equity plus non-current liabilities. Here the company reports 29.2% against an industry average of 21%. The company has proportionately more money tied up in non-current borrowed funds than is the norm in this industry sector. However 29.2% is still relatively low (gearing in excess of 50% indicates a high-geared company) and there is the possibility that more funds could be borrowed to finance future growth and expansion.

The **current ratio** measures the short-term day-to-day financing (liquidity) of the business. Here the company has £3.30 of current assets to cover every £1.00 worth of current liabilities. This is a healthy margin, and is proof that the company does not suffer from any cash flow problems. The ratio is well in excess of the industry average of 1.8.

The **operating profit percentage** measures the profitability of the business. The company reports 7.3% against an industry average of 8%, so it is under-performing in this area. The company could look into its pattern of expenditure to see if any economies can be made which would increase profit and bring it back in line with the sector average. Key items of expenditure in this area are wages and salaries and advertising. The company could also look to reducing its cost of sales – reducing the price it pays for paper, for example.

The **trade payables payment period** measures the average amount of time it takes for the company to pay its suppliers. Here it is paying very promptly with a result of 22.1 days against a sector average of 62 days. It might be suggested that the company could benefit its cash by from extending the terms it obtains from suppliers, especially as liquidity is not a problem.

In conclusion, the company performs better than the sector average in three out of the five ratios. The areas which could be investigated are gearing (which, although higher than the industry norm, is still relatively low), and profitability (where the return is below the industry norm by almost 1%).

8 Consolidated financial statements

8.1   £20,000

8.2   £72,000

8.3   £620,000

8.4   •   **Method of accounting to be used in acquisitions**

The acquisition method is to be used. This measures the cost of the identifiable assets and liabilities being acquired and usually results in the recognition of goodwill.

•   **Assets and liabilities acquired**

The identifiable assets and liabilities being acquired are identified and valued at their fair value on the date of acquisition.

•   **Goodwill**

Goodwill is an asset representing future economic benefits arising from other assets acquired in a business combination that are not individually identified and separately recognised. Goodwill is tested annually for impairment under IAS 36.

Negative goodwill is where the cost of the acquisition is less than the fair value of assets and liabilities acquired. IFRS 3 says that, where negative goodwill is indicated, the first step should be to check the values used to ensure that they are correct. Negative goodwill is recognised in the statement of profit or loss and other comprehensive income immediately.

8.5   **(a)**   IFRS 3, *Business Combinations*, requires that the cost of the business acquired is to be measured at the fair values of all the identifiable* assets and liabilities that existed at the date of acquisition.

Fair value is the price that would be received to sell an asset or paid to transfer a liability in an orderly transaction between market participants at the measurement date. For example, the fair value of land and buildings would be the market value, for plant and equipment it would also be the market value, for raw materials it would be the current replacement cost.

The procedure for dealing with fair values is to restate the subsidiary's statement of financial position using fair values. Increases in the valuation of assets are credited to revaluation reserve; decreases are debited to revaluation reserve. Any changes to the value of liabilities are also passed through revaluation reserve. Note that, to be dealt with in this way, the fair value of identifiable assets and liabilities must be capable of being measured reliably.

*identifiable = either separable from the entity (eg capable of being sold) or arising from contractual or other legal rights.

(b)   Fair value has an effect on the calculations for goodwill, non-controlling interest (where applicable), and sometimes on post-acquisition profits:

·   goodwill, which is the cost of the investment in the subsidiary, less the fair value of the subsidiary's identifiable assets and liabilities

·   non-controlling interest, which is the proportion of the subsidiary, based on the fair value of the subsidiary's identifiable assets and liabilities

·   post-acquisition profits, which will be affected where the use of fair value for non-current assets leads to a different depreciation charge from that based on historic costs

8.6   **Task 1**

Shopan Limited: Consolidated statement of financial position as at 30 September 20-9

ASSETS	£000
Non-current assets	
Goodwill	222
Other non-current assets	8,306
	8,528
Current assets	
Inventories	2,766
Trade receivables	2,102
Cash and cash equivalents	288
	5,156
Total assets	13,684
EQUITY AND LIABILITIES	
Equity	
Share capital	2,000
Share premium	950
Retained earnings	4,246
Equity attributable to equity holders of the parent	7,196
Non-controlling interest	626
Total equity	7,822
Non-current liabilities	
Long-term loan	3,270
	3,270
Current liabilities	
Trade payables	1,973
Tax liability	619
	2,592
Total liabilities	5,862
Total equity and liabilities	13,684

Workings:

1   Shopan Limited holding in Hower Limited

$$\frac{375,000}{500,000} = 75\%$$

Non-controlling interest

$$\frac{125,000}{500,000} = 25\%$$

2   Revaluation of non-current assets in Hower Limited to fair value at date of acquisition:

Debit Non-current assets   £400,000

Credit Revaluation reserve   £400,000

Hence, non-current assets = (6,273,000 + £400,000) + £1,633,000 = £8,306,000

3   Calculation of goodwill arising on consolidation and non-controlling interest:

Goodwill	£000
Share capital – attributable to Shopan Ltd	–375
Share premium – attributable to Shopan Ltd	–90
Revaluation reserve – attributable to Shopan Ltd	–300
Retained earnings – attributable to Shopan Ltd	–1,113
Price paid	2,100
Goodwill =	222

Non-controlling interest (NCI)	£000
Share capital – attributable to NCI	125
Share premium – attributable to NCI	30
Revaluation reserve – attributable to NCI	100
Retained earnings – attributable to NCI	371
Non-controlling interest =	626

Task 2

According to IFRS 10, *Consolidated Financial Statements*, power to direct the relevant activities of the investee include:

- rights in the form of voting rights of an investee (eg a majority – above 50 per cent – of the voting rights – although there may be circumstances where such ownership does not give power).

- rights to appoint, reassign or remove members of an investee's key management personnel who have the ability to direct the relevant activities.

- rights to appoint or remove another entity that directs the relevant activities.

- rights to direct the investee to enter into, or veto any changes to, transactions for the benefit of the investor.

- other rights (eg decision-making rights specified in a management contract) that give the ability to direct the relevant activities.

8.7

Fairway plc and its subsidiary

Consolidated statement of profit or loss for the year ended 30 June 20-2

Continuing operations		£000
Revenue	see working, below	15,600
Cost of sales	see working, below	−10,600
Gross profit		5,000
Distribution costs	£1,600 + £500	−2,100
Administrative expenses	£400 + 200	−600
Profit from operations		2,300
Finance costs	£300 + £200	−500
Profit before tax		1,800
Tax		−500
Profit for the year from continuing operations		1,300

Workings:

Attributable to	£000
Equity holders of the parent £1,300 − £60	1,240
Non-controlling interest 20% x £300*	60
Profit for the period from continuing operations =	1,300

* Green's after-tax profit for the year

Revenue	£000
Fairway plc	12,200
Green Ltd	4,400
Total inter-company adjustment	−1,000
Revenue =	15,600

Cost of sales	£000
Fairway plc	8,500
Green Ltd	3,100
Total inter-company adjustment	−1,000
Cost of sales =	10,600

8.8   **(a)**

Perran Ltd – Consolidated statement of financial position as at 31 March 20X1	
	£000
Assets	
Goodwill	78
Non-current assets	1,570
Current assets	730
Total assets	2,378
Equity and liabilities	
Equity	
Share capital	1,000
Retained earnings	498
Non-controlling interest	180
Total equity	1,678
Non-current liabilities	170
Current liabilities	530
Total liabilities	700
Total equity and liabilities	2,378

Workings:

Goodwill	*£000*
Share capital – attributable to Perran Plc	–480
Retained earnings – attributable to Perran Plc	–192
Price paid	750
Goodwill =	78

Non-controlling interest (NCI)	*£000*
Share capital – attributable to NCI	120
Retained earnings – attributable to NCI	60
Non-controlling interest =	180

Retained earnings	*£000*
Perran Plc	450
Porth Ltd – attributable to Perran Plc	48
Retained earnings =	498

(b)

<table>
<tr><td colspan="2">**Fistral Plc – Consolidated statement of profit or loss
for the year ended 31 March 20X1.**</td></tr>
<tr><td></td><td align="right">*£000*</td></tr>
<tr><td>**Continuing operations**</td><td></td></tr>
<tr><td>Revenue</td><td align="right">24,610</td></tr>
<tr><td>Cost of sales</td><td align="right">−14,830</td></tr>
<tr><td>Gross profit</td><td align="right">9,780</td></tr>
<tr><td>Other income</td><td align="right">−</td></tr>
<tr><td>Distribution costs and administrative expenses</td><td align="right">−5,400</td></tr>
<tr><td>**Profit before tax**</td><td align="right">4,380</td></tr>
</table>

Workings:

Revenue	£000
Fistral Plc	18,250
Beach Ltd	6,450
Total inter-company adjustment	−90
Revenue =	24,610

Cost of sales	£000
Fistral Plc	11,800
Beach Ltd	3,100
Total inter-company adjustment*	−70
Cost of sales =	14,830

* purchases −90, unrealised profit 20[+] = cost of sales −70

[+] unrealised profit is deducted from closing inventories; the effect of this is to increase cost of sales (because closing inventories are deducted in the cost of sales calculation)

Distribution costs and administrative expenses

£3,750,000 + £1,650,000 = £5,400,000

Profit before tax

£3,100,000 + £1,700,000 − £400,000 inter-company dividend − £20,000 unrealised profit

= £4,380,000

Practice
assessment 1

Task 1

You have been asked to help prepare the financial statements of Hanjoy Ltd for the year ended 31 March 20X1. The company's trial balance as at 31 March 20X1 and further information is shown below.

Hanjoy Ltd

Trial balance as at 31 March 20X1

	Debit £000	Credit £000
Share capital		100,000
Revaluation reserve at 1 April 20X0		20,000
Trade and other payables		9,854
Land and buildings – value/cost	125,500	
– accumulated depreciation at 1 April 20X0		15,000
Plant and equipment – cost	40,000	
– accumulated depreciation at 1 April 20X0		14,400
Trade and other receivables	17,234	
Accruals		256
5% bank loans repayable 20X9		20,000
Cash and cash equivalents	7,901	
Retained earnings at 1 April 20X0		9,280
Interest paid	1,000	
Sales revenue		100,497
Purchases	60,191	
Distribution costs	15,348	
Administrative expenses	11,627	
Inventories at 1 April 20X0	8,486	
Dividends paid	2,000	
	289,287	289,287

Further information:

- The inventories at the close of business on 31 March 20X1 cost £9,107,000.

- Land, which is not depreciated, is included in the trial balance at a value of £50,500,000. It is to be revalued at £60,000,000 and this revaluation is to be included in the financial statements for the year ended 31 March 20X1.

- Depreciation is to be provided for the year to 31 March 20X1 as follows:

  | Buildings | 2% per annum | Straight-line basis |
  | Plant and equipment | 20% per annum | Reducing (diminishing) balance basis |

*   Depreciation is to be apportioned as follows:

	%
Cost of sales	50
Distribution costs	20
Administrative expenses	30

*   Trade receivables include a debt of £12,000 which is to be written off. Bad (irrecoverable) debts are to be classified as administrative expenses.

·   Distribution costs of £35,000 owing at 31 March 20X1 are to be provided for.

·   The corporation tax charge for the year has been calculated as £1,827,000.

·   All of the operations are continuing operations.

Required:

(a)   Draft the statement of profit or loss and other comprehensive income for Hanjoy Ltd for the year ended 31 March 20X1.

(b)   Draft the statement of changes in equity for Hanjoy Ltd for the year ended 31 March 20X1.

Note:

You do not need to use the workings to achieve full marks on the task, but data in the workings will be considered if you make errors in the pro-forma.

(You will be asked to draft a statement of financial position in Task 2 using the same data.)

**(a)   Hanjoy Ltd – Statement of profit or loss and other comprehensive income
for the year ended 31 March 20X1**

	£000
Revenue	
Cost of sales	
Gross profit	
Distribution costs	
Administrative expenses	
Profit from operations	
Finance costs	
Profit before tax	
Tax	
Profit for the year from continuing operations	
Other comprehensive income for the year	
Total comprehensive income for the year	

Workings

Cost of sales	£000
Cost of sales =	

Distribution costs	£000
Distribution costs =	

Administrative expenses	£000
Administrative expenses =	

(b)   Hanjoy Ltd – Statement of changes in equity for the year ended 31 March 20X1

	Share Capital £000	Other Reserves £000	Retained Earnings £000	Total Equity £000
Balance at 1 April 20X0				
Changes in equity for 20X1				
Total comprehensive income				
Dividends				
Issue of share capital				
Balance at 31 March 20X1				

Task 2

This task is a continuation of the scenario in Task 1. The same data is used, to which please refer.

You have been asked to prepare the statement of financial position for Hanjoy Ltd as at 31 March 20X1.

Draft the statement of financial position for Hanjoy Ltd as at 31 March 20X1.

Hanjoy Ltd – Statement of financial position as at 31 March 20X1

	£000
ASSETS	
Non-current assets	
Current assets	
Total assets	
EQUITY AND LIABILITIES	
Equity	
Total equity	
Non-current liabilities	
Current liabilities	
Total liabilities	
Total equity and liabilities	

Workings

Property, plant and equipment	£000
Property, plant and equipment =	

Trade and other receivables	£000
Trade and other receivables =	

Trade and other payables	£000
Trade and other payables =	

Retained earnings	£000
Retained earnings =	

Revaluation reserve	£000
Revaluation reserve =	

Task 3(a)

What is the objective of financial statements according to the IASB's *Conceptual Framework for Financial Reporting*.

(b)

Give TWO examples of user groups identified in the Conceptual Framework for Financial Reporting and explain their need for the information in financial statements.

External users	Need for information in financial statements
1.	
2.	

Task 4

The directors of Oak plc are reviewing the accounting treatment for their assets under IAS 36, *Impairment of assets.*

Prepare brief notes for the directors of Oak plc to answer the following points:

(a)

State how, according to IAS 36, an impairment loss is calculated and which two figures are needed.

(b)

Explain what is meant by each of these amounts.

(c)

State how an impairment loss is to be treated in the financial statements.

Task 5

This task consists of one true/false question and five multiple-choice questions.

(a)   A finance lease is where there is no substantial transfer of the risks and rewards of ownership to the lessee.

	✔
True	
False	

(b)   Which one of the following statements best describes the valuation of inventories under IAS 2, *Inventories* at the end of the financial year?

	✔
At the lower of FIFO and AVCO	
At the lower of cost and net realisable value	
At the higher of FIFO and AVCO	
At the higher of cost and net realisable value	

(c)   A business prepares its financial statements to 31 December each year. The following events took place after 31 December but before the date on which the financial statements were authorised for issue:

1.   a significant part of the business is to be discontinued

2.   the net realisable value of inventories is found to be materially below the cost price used in the financial statements

Which of the above is likely to be classified as a non-adjusting event under IAS 10, *Events after the Reporting Period*?

	✔
1 only	
2 only	
1 and 2	
neither 1 nor 2	

(d) Under IAS 16, *Property, Plant and Equipment*, which of the following costs can be included on initial recognition of property, plant and equipment?

1. cost of testing the asset

2. installation and assembly costs

3. purchase price

4. initial delivery and handling costs

	✔
1 and 2	
2 and 3	
3 and 4	
all of them	

(e) Tang Ltd had a profit from operations of £28,000 for the year and the statements of profit or loss and financial position show the following:

	£
depreciation charge	12,000
decrease in inventories	4,000
increase in trade and other receivables	7,000
increase in trade and other payables	3,000
interest paid	2,000
tax paid	9,000

In its statement of cash flows prepared in accordance with IAS 7, what is the amount of Tang's cash from operating activities?

	✔
£40,000	
£29,000	
£37,000	
£51,000	

(f)   In August 20X4, Foss Ltd revalued a piece of land from a cost of £500,000 to its market value of £600,000. There was a decline in the property market and in September 20X7 the market value of the land was £450,000.

In accordance with IAS 36, *Impairment of Assets*, how much of the impairment loss should be recognised in other comprehensive income in the company's statement of profit or loss and other comprehensive income for the year ended 31 December 20X7?

	✔
£100,000	
£150,000	
£50,000	
£NIL	

Task 6

Bravo Plc acquired 75% of the issued share capital and voting rights of Salvo Ltd on 1 April 20X0 for £1,600,000. At that date Salvo Ltd had issued share capital of £1,000,000 and retained earnings of £480,000.

Extracts from the statements of financial position for the two companies one year later at 31 March 20X1 are as follows:

	Bravo Plc £000	Salvo Ltd £000
Assets		
Investment in Salvo Ltd	1,600	
Property, plant and equipment	2,050	1,620
Current assets	1,400	390
Total assets	5,050	2,010
Equity and liabilities		
Equity		
Share capital	2,000	1,000
Retained earnings	1,900	640
Total equity	3,900	1,640
Non-current liabilities	350	220
Current liabilities	800	150
Total liabilities	1,150	370
Total equity and liabilities	5,050	2,010

Further information:

- Included within the current assets of Bravo Plc and in the current liabilities of Salvo Ltd is an inter-company transaction for £50,000 that took place in early March 20X1.
- Bravo Plc has decided non-controlling interest will be valued at their proportionate share of net assets.

(a)

Draft the consolidated statement of financial position for Bravo Plc and its subsidiary undertaking as at 31 March 20X1. Use the layout shown below.

Bravo Plc – Consolidated statement of financial position as at 31 March 20X1

	£000
ASSETS	
Non-current assets	
Goodwill	
Property, plant and equipment	
Current assets	
Inventories	
Trade receivables	
Cash and cash equivalents	
Total assets	
EQUITY AND LIABILITIES	
Equity	
Share capital	
Share premium	
Retained earnings	
Non-controlling interest	
Total equity	
Non-current liabilities	
Current liabilities	
Total liabilities	
Total equity and liabilities	

Workings:

Goodwill	£000
Goodwill =	

Non-controlling interest (NCI)	£000
Non-controlling interest =	

Retained earnings	£000
Retained earnings =	

Weiss Plc acquired 80% of the issued share capital of Hirsh Ltd on 1 April 20X0.

Extracts from their statements of profit or loss for the year ended 31 March 20X1 are shown below:

	Weiss Plc £000	Hirsh Ltd £000
Continuing operations		
Revenue	30,400	10,300
Cost of sales	−17,800	−6,100
Gross profit	12,600	4,200
Other income – dividend from Hirsh Ltd	500	–
Distribution costs	−3,000	−1,000
Administrative expenses	−1,500	−800
Profit before tax	8,600	2,400

Further information:

During the year Hirsh Ltd sold goods which had cost £40,000 to Weiss Plc for £100,000. Half of these goods still remain in inventory at the end of the year.

(b)

Draft the consolidated statement of profit or loss for Weiss Plc and its subsidiary undertaking up to and including the profit before tax line for the year ended 31 March 20X1. Use the layout shown below.

Weiss Plc – Consolidated statement of profit or loss for the year ended 31 March 20X1

	£000
Continuing operations	
Revenue	
Cost of sales	
Gross profit	
Other income	
Distribution costs	
Administrative expenses	
Profit from operations	
Finance costs	
Profit before tax	

Workings

Revenue	£000
Parent	
Subsidiary	
Total inter-company adjustment*	
Revenue =	

* enter '0' if no adjustment needed

Cost of sales	£000
Parent	
Subsidiary	
Total inter-company adjustment*	
Cost of sales =	

* enter '0' if no adjustment needed

Task 7

You have been asked to calculate ratios for Nelson Ltd in respect of its financial statements for the year ending 31 March 20X1 to assist your manager in his analysis of the company.

Nelson Ltd's statement of profit or loss and statement of financial position are set out below.

Nelson Ltd – Statement of profit or loss for the year ended 31 March 20X1

	20X1
	£000
Continuing operations	
Revenue	32,400
Cost of sales	−17,982
Gross profit	14,418
Distribution costs	−7,319
Administrative expenses	−4,345
Profit from operations	2,754
Finance costs	−459
Profit before tax	2,295
Tax	−531
Profit for the year from continuing operations	1,764

Nelson Ltd – Statement of financial position as at 31 March 20X1

	20X1 £000
ASSETS	
Non-current assets	
Property, plant and equipment	49,369
Current assets	
Inventories	1,684
Trade receivables	2,833
Cash and cash equivalents	114
	4,631
Total assets	54,000
EQUITY AND LIABILITIES	
Equity	
Share capital	35,000
Retained earnings	15,400
Total equity	50,400
Non-current liabilities	
Bank loans	1,495
	1,495
Current liabilities	
Trade payables	1,574
Tax liability	531
	2,105
Total liabilities	3,600
Total equity and liabilities	54,000

Using the form on the next page:

(a) State the formulas that are used to calculate each of the following ratios:

    (1) Return on shareholders' funds

    (2) Current ratio

    (3) Asset turnover (net assets)

    (4) Gearing

    (5) Interest cover

(b) Calculate the above ratios (to the nearest one decimal place).

Ratio	(a) Formula	(b) Calculation of ratio for Nelson Ltd
(1) Return on share-holders' funds		
(2) Current ratio		
(3) Asset turnover (net assets)		
(4) Gearing		
(5) Interest cover		

Task 8

Steve Horan is a shareholder in Blenheim Ltd and has asked you to assist him in assessing the efficiency and effectiveness of the management of the company. You have calculated the following ratios in respect of Blenheim Ltd's financial statements for the last two years to assist you in your analysis.

	20X1	20X0
Gross profit percentage	42.0%	45.0%
Operating profit percentage	9.5%	7.5%
Inventory holding period	84 days	66 days
Trade receivables collection period	55 days	40 days
Trade payables payment period	50 days	42 days

Prepare a report to Steve that includes:

(a)

A comment on the relative performance of the company for the two years based on the ratios calculated and what this tells you about the company

---

REPORT

To: Steve Horan
From: AAT student
Subject: Shareholding in Blenheim Ltd
Date: Today

---

if required, continue on next page

(b)

Advise, with reasons based on the ratios you have calculated, on whether or not Steve should maintain his investment in the company

Practice
assessment 2

Task 1

You have been asked to prepare the statement of cash flows and statement of changes in equity for Kneale Ltd for the year ended 31 March 20X1.

The most recent statement of profit or loss and statements of financial position for the company are set out below.

Kneale Ltd – Statement of profit or loss for the year ended 31 March 20X1

	£000
Continuing operations	
Revenue	108,000
Cost of sales	−80,500
Gross profit	27,500
Gain on disposal of property, plant and equipment	112
Distribution costs	−11,214
Administrative expenses	−14,618
Profit from operations	1,780
Finance costs	−693
Profit before tax	1,087
Tax	−214
Profit/Loss for the year from continuing operations	873

Kneale Ltd – Statements of financial position as at 31 March

	20X1 £000	20X0 £000
Assets		
Non-current assets		
Property, plant and equipment	7,610	6,325
Current assets		
Inventories	2,544	2,795
Trade receivables	3,728	3,419
Cash and cash equivalents	0	312
	6,272	6,526
Total assets	13,882	12,851
EQUITY AND LIABILITIES		
Equity		
Share capital	2,500	1,500
Share premium	410	210
Retained earnings	6,566	6,043
Total equity	9,476	7,753
Non-current liabilities		
Bank loans	750	2,500
	750	2,500
Current liabilities		
Trade payables	3,025	2,107
Tax liabilities	214	491
Bank overdraft	417	0
	3,656	2,598
Total liabilities	4,406	5,098
Total equity and liabilities	13,882	12,851

Further information:

- The total depreciation charge for the year was £727,000.
- Property, plant and equipment costing £225,000 with accumulated depreciation of £152,000 was sold in the year.
- All sales and purchases were on credit. Other expenses were paid for in cash.
- A dividend of £350,000 was paid during the year.

(a) Prepare a reconciliation of profit from operations to net cash from operating activities for Kneale Ltd for the year ended 31 March 20X1. Use the layout shown on the next page.

(b) Prepare the statement of cash flows for Kneale Ltd for the year ended 31 March 20X1. Use the layout shown on page 109.

Note:

You do not need to use the workings to achieve full marks on the task, but data in the workings will be considered if you make errors in the pro-forma.

(You will be asked to draft a statement of changes in equity in Task 2 using the same data.)

(a) **Kneale Ltd**

Reconciliation of profit from operations to net cash from operating activities

	£000
Profit from operations	
Adjustments for:	
Cash generated by operations	
Net cash from operating activities	

(b) **Kneale Ltd**

Statement of cash flows for the year ended 31 March 20X1

	£000
Net cash from operating activities	
Investing activities	
Net cash used in investing activities	
Financing activities	
Net cash used in financing activities	
Net increase/decrease in cash and cash equivalents	
Cash and cash equivalents at beginning of year	
Cash and cash equivalents at end of year	

Workings:

Proceeds on disposal of property, plant and equipment	£000
Proceeds =	

Purchases of property, plant and equipment	£000
Total property, plant and equipment additions =	

Task 2

This task is a continuation of the scenario in Task 1. The same data is used, to which please refer.

You have been asked to prepare the statement of changes in equity for Kneale Ltd for the year ended 31 March 20X1.

Draft the statement of changes in equity for Kneale Ltd for the year ended 31 March 20X1.

Kneale Ltd – Statement of changes in equity for the year ended 31 March 20X1

	Share Capital	Other Reserves	Retained Earnings	Total Equity
	£000	£000	£000	£000
Balance at start of the year				
Changes in equity for the year				
Profit for the year				
Dividends				
Issue of share capital				
Balance at end of the year				

Task 3

(a)

According to the IASB's *Conceptual Framework for Financial Reporting*, what are the two fundamental qualitative characteristics that make financial information useful?

1.	
2.	

(b)

Explain what is meant by each of the two fundamental qualitative characteristics.

Task 4

The directors of Wentworth plc are reviewing their assets under IAS 38, *Intangible Assets.*

Prepare brief notes for the directors of Wentworth plc to answer the following points:

(a)

What is the definition of an intangible asset?

(b)

Give **TWO** examples of an intangible asset.

(c)

State and explain the **THREE** key elements of an intangible asset.

Task 5

This task consists of one true/false question and five multiple-choice questions.

(a)   In accordance with IAS 37, *Provisions, Contingent Liabilities and Contingent Assets*, a contingent asset should be disclosed in the notes to the financial statements only where the inflow of economic benefits is probable.

	✔
True	
False	

(b)   A business holds three distinct types of inventory in its warehouse at the end of its financial year. These are valued as follows:

Inventory	FIFO (cost) £	LIFO (cost) £	NRV £
Type R	3,400	3,300	5,200
Type S	1,950	2,050	3,250
Type T	2,600	2,500	2,450
Total	7,950	7,850	10,900

To comply with IAS 2, *Inventories*, indicate the value at which the inventory should be stated in the financial statements.

	✔
£7,700	
£7,800	
£7,850	
£7,950	

(c) Under IAS 17, *Leases*, how should finance leases be recognised as liabilities on a lessee's statement of financial position?

	✔
at the higher of fair value less costs to sell and value in use of the asset being leased	
at the higher of the fair value of the asset being leased and the present value of the minimum lease payments	
at the lower of the fair value of the asset being leased and the present value of the minimum lease payments	
at the value in use of the asset being leased	

(d) A limited company has purchased a new machine with the following expenditure:

	£
Invoice price of the machine	18,750
Delivery costs	550
Administration costs	600
Cost of testing the machine	1,100
Total expenditure	21,000

Under IAS 16, *Property, Plant and Equipment*, what cost will the company include in property, plant and equipment?

	✔
£19,300	
£19,900	
£20,400	
£21,000	

(e)   According to IAS 18, *Revenue*, how is revenue to be measured?

	✔
at the fair value of the consideration received or receivable	
at the lower of cost and net realisable value	
at cost or revaluation, less impairment losses	
at the amount of cash and cash equivalents received	

(f)   A business prepares its financial statements to 31 March each year. The following events took place after 31 March but before the date on which the financial statements were authorised for issue:

1.   a major customer who owes money to the company at the end of the financial year is declared bankrupt

2.   a non-current asset has had to be replaced at considerable cost

Which of the above is likely to be classified as an adjusting event under IAS 10, *Events after the Reporting Period*?

	✔
1 only	
2 only	
1 and 2	
neither 1 nor 2	

Task 6

Severn Plc acquired 60% of the issued share capital and voting rights of Teme Ltd on 1 April 20X0 for £700,000. At that date Teme Ltd had issued share capital of £700,000 and retained earnings of £250,000.

Extracts from the statements of financial position for the two companies one year later at 31 March 20X1 are as follows:

	Severn Plc £000	Teme Ltd £000
Assets		
Investment in Teme Ltd	700	
Property, plant and equipment	1,800	1,000
Current assets	760	360
Total assets	3,260	1,360
Equity and liabilities		
Equity		
Share capital	2,000	700
Retained earnings	650	310
Total equity	2,650	1,010
Non-current liabilities	120	200
Current liabilities	490	150
Total liabilities	610	350
Total equity and liabilities	3,260	1,360

Further information

- Included within the current assets of Severn Plc and in the current liabilities of Teme Ltd is an inter-company transaction for £20,000 that took place in early March 20X1.
- Severn Plc has decided non-controlling interest will be valued at their proportionate share of net assets.

(a)

Draft the consolidated statement of financial position for Severn Plc and its subsidiary undertaking as at 31 March 20X1. Use the layout shown below.

Note: You do not need to use the workings to achieve full marks on the task, but data in the workings will be considered if you make errors in the pro-forma.

Severn Plc – Consolidated statement of financial position as at 31 March 20X1

	£000
ASSETS	
Non-current assets	
Goodwill	
Property, plant and equipment	
Current assets	
Total assets	
EQUITY AND LIABILITIES	
Equity	
Share capital	
Retained earnings	
Non-controlling interest	
Total equity	
Non-current liabilities	
Current liabilities	
Total liabilities	
Total equity and liabilities	

Workings

Goodwill	£000
Goodwill =	

Non-controlling interest (NCI)	£000
Non-controlling interest =	

Retained earnings	£000
Retained earnings =	

Sinton Plc acquired 75% of the issued share capital and voting rights of Green Ltd on 1 April 20X0.

Extracts from their statements of profit or loss for the year ended 31 March 20X1 are shown below:

	Sinton Plc	Green Ltd
	£000	£000
Continuing operations		
Revenue	48,400	17,200
Cost of sales	–31,200	–9,800
Gross profit	17,200	7,400
Other income – dividend from Green Ltd	500	–
Distribution costs	–8,000	–3,200
Administrative expenses	–4,200	–1,000
Profit before tax	5,500	3,200

Further information:

During the year Green Ltd sold goods which had cost £50,000 to Sinton Plc for £80,000. Two-thirds of these goods still remain in inventory at the end of the year.

(b)

Draft the consolidated statement of profit or loss for Sinton Plc and its subsidiary undertaking up to and including the profit before tax line for the year ended 31 March 20X1. Use the layout shown below.

Note:
You do not need to use the workings to achieve full marks on the task, but data in the workings will be considered if you make errors in the pro-forma.

Sinton Plc – Consolidated statement of profit or loss for the year ended 31 March 20X1

	£000
Continuing operations	
Revenue	
Cost of sales	
Gross profit	
Other income	
Distribution costs	
Administrative expenses	
Profit from operations	
Finance costs	
Profit before tax	

Workings:

Revenue	£000
Parent	
Subsidiary	
Total inter-company adjustment*	
Revenue =	

* enter '0' if no adjustment needed

Cost of sale	£000
Parent	
Subsidiary	
Total inter-company adjustment*	
Cost of sales =	

* enter '0' if no adjustment needed

Task 7

You have been asked to calculate ratios for Laceby Ltd in respect of its financial statements for the year ending 31 March 20X1 to assist your manager in his analysis of the company.

Laceby Ltd's statement of profit or loss and statement of financial position are set out below.

Laceby Ltd – Statement of profit or loss for the year ended 31 March 20X1

	20X1
	£000
Continuing operations	
Revenue	45,300
Cost of sales	–22,620
Gross profit	22,680
Distribution costs	–8,345
Administrative expenses	–10,052
Profit from operations	4,283
Finance costs	–964
Profit before tax	3,319
Tax	–623
Profit for the year from continuing operations	2,696

Laceby Ltd – Statement of financial position as at 31 March 20X1

	20X1 £000
ASSETS	
Non-current assets	
Property, plant and equipment	77,094
Current assets	
Inventories	2,514
Trade receivables	3,986
Cash and cash equivalents	1,522
	8,022
Total assets	85,116
EQUITY AND LIABILITIES	
Equity	
Share capital	60,000
Retained earnings	9,685
Total equity	69,685
Non-current liabilities	
Bank loans	12,093
	12,093
Current liabilities	
Trade payables	2,715
Tax liability	623
	3,338
Total liabilities	15,431
Total equity and liabilities	85,116

Using the form on the next page:

(a)   State the formulas that are used to calculate each of the following ratios:

   (1)   Gross profit percentage
   (2)   Acid test (quick) ratio
   (3)   Asset turnover (non-current assets)
   (4)   Inventory holding period (days)
   (5)   Trade payables payment period

(b)   Calculate the above ratios (to the nearest one decimal place)

Ratio	(a) Formula	(b) Calculation of ratio for Laceby Ltd
(1) Gross profit percentage		
(2) Acid test (quick) ratio		
(3) Asset turnover (non-current assets)		
(4) Inventory holding period (days)		
(5) Trade payables payment period		

Task 8

Louise Forsythe is a shareholder in Kingham Ltd and has asked you to assist her in assessing the effectiveness of the management of the company in using its resources. You have calculated the following ratios in respect of Kingham Ltd's financial statements for the last two years to assist you in your analysis.

	20X1	20X0
Gross profit percentage	39.0%	42.0%
Operating profit percentage	10.0%	9.5%
Return on shareholders' funds	12.0%	10.5%
Gearing	22.2%	27.4%
Interest cover	10.6 times	9.1 times

Prepare a report to Louise that includes:

(a)

A comment on the relative performance of the company for the two years based on the ratios calculated and what this tells you about the company.

REPORT

To: Louise Forsythe
From: AAT student
Subject: Shareholding in Kingham Ltd
Date: Today

if required, continue on next page

(b)

Advise, with reasons based on the ratios you have calculated, on whether or not Louise should maintain her investment in the company.

Practice
assessment 3

Task 1

You have been asked to prepare the statement of cash flows and statement of changes in equity for Chen Ltd for the year ended 31 March 20X1.

The most recent statement of profit or loss and statement of financial position (with comparatives for the previous year) of Chen Ltd are set out below.

Chen Ltd – Statement of profit or loss for the year ended 31 March 20X1

Continuing operations	£000
Revenue	65,200
Cost of sales	−31,860
Gross profit	33,340
Dividends received	84
Loss on disposal of property, plant and equipment	-40
Distribution costs	−15,627
Administrative expenses	−7,983
Profit from operations	9,774
Finance costs	−212
Profit before tax	9,562
Tax	−3,367
Profit for the year from continuing operations	6,195

Chen Ltd – Statement of financial position as at 31 March 20X1

	20X1 £000	20X0 £000
ASSETS		
Non-current assets		
Property, plant and equipment	39,630	32,860
Current assets		
Inventories	5,796	4,124
Trade receivables	7,041	6,732
Cash and cash equivalents	0	430
	12,837	11,286
Total assets	52,467	44,146

EQUITY AND LIABILITIES		
Equity		
Share capital	12,000	10,000
Share premium	5,000	4,000
Retained earnings	27,390	21,749
Total equity	44,390	35,749
Non-current liabilities		
Bank loans	1,250	3,000
	1,250	3,000
Current liabilities		
Trade payables	3,176	3,249
Tax liabilities	3,367	2,148
Bank overdraft	284	0
	7,827	5,397
Total liabilities	8,077	8,397
Total equity and liabilities	52,467	44,146

Further information:

The total depreciation charge for the year was £4,275,000.

Property, plant and equipment costing £655,000 with accumulated depreciation of £231,000 was sold in the year.

All sales and purchases were on credit. Other expenses were paid for in cash.

A dividend of £554,000 was paid during the year.

(a)   Prepare a reconciliation of profit from operations to net cash from operating activities for Chen Ltd for the year ended 31 March 20X1. Use the layout shown on the next page.

(b)   Prepare the statement of cash flows for Chen Ltd for the year ended 31 March 20X1. Use the layout shown on page 131.

Note:

You don't need to use the workings to achieve full marks on the task, but data in the workings will be considered if you make errors in the pro-forma.

(You will be asked to draft a statement of changes in equity in Task 2 using the same data.)

Chen Ltd

Reconciliation of profit from operations to net cash from operating activities

	£000
Profit from operations	
Adjustments for:	
Cash generated by operations	
Net cash from operating activities	

Chen Ltd

Statement of cash flows for the year ended 31 March 20X1

	£000
Net cash from operating activities	
Investing activities	
Net cash used in investing activities	
Financing activities	
Net cash from financing activities	
Net increase/decrease in cash and cash equivalents	
Cash and cash equivalents at beginning of year	
Cash and cash equivalents at end of year	

Workings:

Proceeds on disposal of property, plant and equipment	£000
Proceeds =	

Purchases of property, plant and equipment	£000
Total property, plant and equipment additions=	

Task 2

This task is a continuation of the scenario in Task 1. The same data is used, to which please refer.

You have been asked to prepare the statement of changes in equity for Chen Ltd for the year ended 31 March 20X1.

Draft the statement of changes in equity for Chen Ltd for the year ended 31 March 20X1.

Chen Ltd – Statement of changes in equity for the year ended 31 March 20X1

	Share capital £000	Share premium £000	Retained earnings £000	Total equity £000
Balance at 1 April 20X0				
Changes in equity for 20X1				
Profit for the year				
Dividends				
Issue of share capital				
Balance at 31 March 20X1				

Task 3

(a)   What is the objective of general purpose financial reporting according to IASB's *Conceptual Framework for Financial Reporting*?

(b)   Give **ONE** decision that might be made by EACH user of financial statements and which is helped by information contained in the financial statements.

Task 4

With reference to IAS 16, *Propertty, Plant and Equipment,* you are to:

(a)   State how property, plany and equipment is defined.

(b)   Describe the two models available to an entity as its accounting policy.

(c)   Explain how a revaluation increase is dealt with in the financial statements.

(d)   Explain how a revaluation decrease is dealt with in the financial statements.

Task 5

This task consists of one true/false question and five multiple choice questions.

(a) Lopez Ltd has discontinued a significant part of its business after the financial year end of 31 December 20X4 but before the date the financial statements are authorised for issue.

Under IAS 10, *Events after the Reporting Period*, this is an adjusting event.

✓

True	
False	

(b) Under IAS 1, *Presentation of Financial Statements*, which of the following must be indentified?

1. going concern
2. accrual basis of accounting
3. consistency of presentation
4. comparative information

✓

None of them	
1, 2, and 3	
1, 2 and 4	
All of them	

(c) Hamid Ltd has four assets which the directors wish to test for impairment:

asset	carrying amount £	fair value, less costs of disposal £	value in use £
1	20,000	21,000	19,000
2	15,000	12,000	14,000
3	33,000	35,000	30,000
4	26,000	22,000	25,000

Which of the above assets is impaired according to IAS 36, *Impairment of Assets*?

	✓
1	
2	
1 and 3	
2 and 4	

(d) IAS 38, *Intangible Assets*, gives three key elements of an intangible asset.

What are the three key elements of an intangible asset?

	✓
identifiability, future economic benefits, control	
control, reliability, understandability	
future economic benefits, reliability, comparability	
identifiability, comparability, reliability	

(e) AB Ltd has the following year end valuations for the two group of inventory in which it trades:

	Cost	Net Realisable Value
	£	£
Inventory A	12,500	18,500
Inventory B	15,000	14,500
Total	27,500	33,000

Under IAS 2, *Inventories*, which **ONE** of the following valuations is correct?

	✓
£27,000	
£27,500	
£33,000	
£33,500	

(f) Sabine Ltd purchased an item of plant for £340,000 on 1 January 20X1. The useful life was anticipated as being 6 years and the residual value was estimated as £100,000. Sabine Ltd depreciates plant on a straight-line basis.

The residual value was still considered to be £100,000 at 1 January 20X4, but the remaining useful life was reassessed to be 4 years.

Under IAS 16, *Property, plant and equipment,* what is the depreciation charge for the item of plant for the current year to 31 December 20X4?

	✓
£25,000	
£30,000	
£40,000	
£60,000	

Task 6

Lee Plc acquired 75% of the issued share capital and voting rights of Shaw Ltd on 1 January 20X0 for £3,400,000. At that date Shaw Ltd had issued share capital of £2,000,000, share premium of £500,000 and retained earnings of £420,000.

Extracts from the statements of financial position for the two companies one year later at 31 December 20X0 are as follows:

	Lee Plc	Shaw Ltd
	£000	£000
ASSETS		
Non-current assets		
Investment in Shaw Ltd	3,550	
Property, plant and equipment	2,745	3,420
	6,295	3,420
Current Assets	1,690	1,497
Total assets	7,985	4,917
EQUITY AND LIABILITIES		
Equity		
Share capital	3,500	2,000
Share premium	750	500
Retained earnings	1,390	540
Total equity	5,640	3,040
Non-current liabilities	300	255
Current liabilities	2,045	1,622
Total liabilities	2,345	1,877
Total equity and liabilities	**7,985**	**4,917**

Further information:

Lee Plc has decided non-controlling interest will be valued at their proportionate share of net assets.

At 1 January 20X0 the fair value of the non-current assets of Shaw Ltd was £200,000 more than the book value. This revaluation has not been recorded in the books of Shaw Ltd (ignore any effect on the depreciation for the year).

On 1 October 20X0, Lee Plc made an interest-free long-term loan of £150,000 to Shaw Ltd, and classified it as part of its investment in Shaw Ltd. Shaw Ltd has classified the loan as a non-current liability in its Financial Statements. No loan repayments has yet been made.

The directors of Lee Plc have calculated that goodwill has been impaired by £120,000 during the year.

Draft the consolidated statement of financial position for Lee Plc and its subsidiary undertaking as at 31 December 20X0.

Note:

You don't need to use the workings to achieve full marks on the task, but data in the workings will be considered if you make errors in the pro-forma.

Lee Plc – Consolidated Statement of financial position as at 31 December 20X0

	£000
ASSETS	
Non-current assets	
Goodwill	
Property, plant and equipment	
Current assets	
Total assets	
EQUITY AND LIABILITIES	
Equity	
Share capital	
Share premium	
Retained earnings	
Non-controlling interest	
Total equity	
Non-current liabilities	
Current liabilities	
Total liabilities	
Total equity and liabilities	

Workings:

Goodwill	£000
Goodwill =	

Non-controlling interest (NCI)	£000
Non-controlling interest =	

Retained earnings	£000
Retained earnings =	

Task 7

You have been given the financial statements of Dodia Ltd for the year ending 31 December 20X0. You are now required to prepare financial ratios to assist your manager in her analysis of the company.

Dodia Ltd's statement of profit or loss and statement of financial position are set out below.

Dodia Ltd – Statement of profit or loss for the year ended 31 March 20X0

	20X0
	£000
Continuing operations	
Revenue	64,300
Cost of sales	−39,163
Gross profit	25,137
Distribution costs	−10,410
Administrative expenses	−7,380
Profit from operations	7,347
Finance costs	−1,054
Profit before tax	6,293
Tax	−2,048
Profit for the year from continuing operations	4,245

Dodia Ltd – Statement of financial position as at 31 March 20X0

	20X0
	£000
ASSETS	
Non-current assets	
Property, plant and equipment	28,800
Current assets	
Inventories	3,695
Trade receivables	4,568
Cash and cash equivalents	1,075
	9,338
Total assets	38,138
EQUITY AND LIABILITIES	
Equity	
Ordinary share capital (£1 share)	20,000
Retained earnings	10,416
Total equity	30,416
Non-current liabilities	
Bank loans	2,500
	2,500
Current liabilities	
Trade payables	3,174
Tax liabilities	2,048
	5,222
Total liabilities	7,722
Total equity and liabilities	38,138

Note: there have been no share issues during the year.

Using the form below:

(a) State the formulas that are used to calculate each of the following ratios:

> **(1)** Operating profit percentage
>
> **(2)** Acid test (quick) ratio
>
> **(3)** Asset turnover (net assets) (times)
>
> **(4)** Trade payables payment period (days)
>
> **(5)** Interest cover (times)

(b) Calculate the above ratios (to the nearest one decimal place).

Ratio	(a) Formula	(b) Calculation of ratio for Dodia Ltd
(1) Operating profit percentage		
(2) Acid test (quick) ratio		
(3) Asset turnover (net assets)		
(4) Trade payables payment period		
(5) Interest cover		

Task 8

Joanna Fonseca, the Managing Director of Faloye Ltd, is concerned that the company is not managing its working capital efficiently. She has sent you an email asking for your assistance in identifying any problem area(s) and for your suggestions as to how these can be remedied.

You have calculated the following ratios in respect of Faloye Ltd's latest financial statements and have also obtained the industry average for each of these for comparative purposes.

	Faloye Ltd	**Industry Average**
Current ratio	1.6:1	2.1:1
Inventory holding period	37 days	35 days
Trade receivables collection period	38 days	39 days
Trade payables payment period	53 days	44 days

Using the form on the next page prepare an email reply to Joanna that includes:

(a)   Comments on whether Faloye Ltd has performed better or worse, in respect of the calculated ratios, as compared to the industry averages.

(b)   **THREE** suggestions as to how the working capital of Faloye Ltd could be more effectively managed.

email

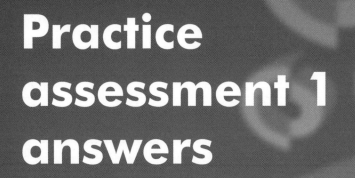

Practice
assessment 1
answers

Task 1

(a) **Hanjoy Ltd – Statement of profit or loss and other comprehensive income for the year ended 31 March 20X1**

	£000
Revenue	100,497
Cost of sales	−62,880
Gross profit	37,617
Distribution costs	−16,707
Administrative expenses	−13,625
Profit from operations	7,285
Finance costs	−1,000
Profit before tax	6,285
Tax	−1,827
Profit for the year from continuing operations	4,458
Other comprehensive income for the year	9,500
Total comprehensive income for the year	13,958

Workings:

Cost of sales	£000
Opening inventories	8,486
Purchases	60,191
Closing inventories	−9,107
Depreciation	*3,310
Cost of sales =	62,880

* depreciation: buildings £75,000 x 2% x 50% = £750; plant and equipment (£40,000 − £14,400) x 20% x 50% = £2,560; total £3,310

Distribution costs	£000
Distribution costs	15,348
Accrual	35
Depreciation	*1,324
Distribution costs =	16,707

* depreciation as per cost of sales, but at 20%

Administrative expenses	£000
Administrative expenses	11,627
Bad (irrecoverable) debt	12
Depreciation	*1,986
Administrative expenses =	13,625

* depreciation as per cost of sales, but at 30%

(b)   Hanjoy Ltd – Statement of changes in equity for the year ended 31 March 20X1

	Share Capital	Other Reserves	Retained Earnings	Total Equity
	£000	£000	£000	£000
Balance at 1 April 20X0	100,000	20,000	9,280	129,280
Changes in equity for 20X1				
Total comprehensive income		9,500	4,458	13,958
Dividends			–2,000	–2,000
Issue of share capital				
Balance at 31 March 20X1	100,000	29,500	11,738	141,238

Task 2

Hanjoy Ltd – Statement of financial position as at 31 March 20X1

	£000
Assets	
Non-current assets	
Property, plant and equipment	138,980
Current assets	
Inventories	9,107
Trade and other receivables	17,222
Cash and cash equivalents	7,901
	34,230
Total assets	173,210
EQUITY AND LIABILITIES	
Equity	
Share capital	100,000
Retained earnings	11,738
Revaluation reserve	29,500
Total equity	141,238
Non-current liabilities	
Bank loans	20,000
	20,000
Current liabilities	
Trade and other payables	10,145
Tax liability	1,827
	11,972
Total liabilities	31,972
Total equity and liabilities	173,210

Workings:

Property, plant and equipment	£000
Land and buildings – value	125,500
Accumulated depreciation – land and buildings	*–16,500
Revaluation – land and buildings	9,500
Plant and equipment – cost	40,000
Accumulated depreciation – plant and equipment	**–19,520
Property, plant and equipment =	138,980

* £15,000 + £1,500

** £14,400 + £5,120

Trade and other receivables	£000
Trade and other receivables	17,234
Bad (irrecoverable) debt	–12
Trade and other receivables =	17,222

Trade and other payables	£000
Trade and other payables	9,854
Accruals – trial balance	256
Additional costs accrued	*35
Trade and other payables =	10,145

* distribution costs accrued

Task 3

(a)

> The objective of financial reporting according to the IASB's *Conceptual Framework for Financial Reporting* is 'to provide financial information about the reporting entity that is useful to existing and potential investors, lenders and other creditors in making decisions about providing resources to the entity.'

(b)

User groups **TWO** from:	Need for information in financial statements
Existing and potential investors	– to help determine whether to buy, hold or sell shares – to assess the stewardship of management – to assess the ability of the entity to pay dividends – to see if the entity will continue in the foreseeable future – to see if the entity is expanding or declining
Lenders	– to check if the entity will be able to pay finance costs and make loan repayments – to assess how far the lender is financing the company – to assess the value of security available to the lender
Other creditors	– to decide whether to supply goods and services to the entity – to assess if the entity is able to pay its debts

Task 4

(a)

An impairment loss is the amount by which the carrying amount of an asset exceeds its recoverable amount. The loss is calculated as the difference between the asset's recoverable amount and its carrying amount.

(b)

'Carrying amount' is the amount at which an asset is recognised in the statement of financial position after deducting any accumulated depreciation (amortisation) and accumulated impairment losses.
'Recoverable amount' of an asset is the higher of its fair value, less costs of disposal, and its value in use. The latter is the present value of the future cash flows expected to be derived from the asset, including cash from its ultimate disposal.

(c)

The value of the asset is reduced to its recoverable amount in the statement of financial position and the impairment loss is recognised immediately in the statement of comprehensive income (unless it relates to a previously revalued asset, when it is recognised as a decrease in other comprehensive income and is debited to the revaluation surplus within equity).

Task 5

(a)   False

(b)   at the lower of cost and net realisable value

(c)   1 only

(d)   all of them

(e)   £29,000

(f)   £100,000 (Tutorial note: impairment loss of £150,000 for 20X7, £50,000 recognised as an expense, £100,000 recognised as a decrease in other comprehensive income and debited to the previously-created revaluation surplus, ie the extent of the revaluation surplus for the asset).

Task 6(a)   **Bravo Plc – Consolidated statement of financial position as at 31 March 20X1**

	£000
ASSETS	
Non-current assets	
Goodwill	490
Property, plant and equipment	3,670
	4,160
Current assets	1,740
Inventories	
Trade receivables	
Cash and cash equivalents	
	1,740
Total assets	5,900
EQUITY AND LIABILITIES	
Equity	
Share capital	2,000
Share premium	
Retained earnings	2,020
Non-controlling interest	410
Total equity	4,430
Non-current liabilities	570
Current liabilities	900
Total liabilities	1,470
Total equity and liabilities	5,900

Workings:

Goodwill	£000
Share capital – attributable to parent	–750
Retained earnings – attributable to parent	–360
Price paid	1,600
Goodwill =	490

Non-controlling interest	£000
Share capital – attributable to NCI	250
Retained earnings – attributable to NCI	160
Non-controlling interest =	410

Retained earnings	£000
Parent	1,900
Subsidiary – attributable to parent	120
Retained earnings =	2,020

Inter-company transaction

£50,000 deducted from the current assets of Bravo Plc and from the current liabilities of Salvo Ltd

(b) **Weiss Plc – Consolidated statement of profit or loss for the year ended 31 March 20X1**

	£000
Continuing operations	
Revenue	40,600
Cost of sales	−23,830
Gross profit	16,770
Other income	0
Distribution costs	−4,000
Administrative expenses	−2,300
Profit from operations	10,470
Finance costs	0
Profit before tax	10,470

Workings:

Revenue	£000
Parent	30,400
Subsidiary	10,300
Total inter-company adjustment	−100
Revenue =	40,600

Cost of sales	£000
Parent	17,800
Subsidiary	6,100
Total inter-company adjustment*	−70
Cost of sales =	23,830

* purchases −100, unrealised profit 30$^+$ = cost of sales −70

$^+$unrealised profit is deducted from closing inventories; the effect of this is to increase cost of sales (because closing inventories are deducted in the cost of sales calculation)

Distribution costs
£3,000,000 + £1,000,000 = £4,000,000

Administrative expenses
£1,500,000 + £800,000 = £2,300,000

Profit before tax
£8,600,000 + £2,400,000 − £500,000 inter-company dividend − £30,000 unrealised profit
= £10,470,000

Task 7

Ratio	(a) Formula	(b) Calculation of ratio for Nelson Ltd
(1) Return on shareholders' funds	$\dfrac{\text{Profit after tax}}{\text{Total equity}} \times 100$	$\dfrac{1{,}764}{50{,}400} \times 100 \quad = \quad 3.5\%$
(2) Current ratio	$\dfrac{\text{Current assets}}{\text{Current liabilities}}$	$\dfrac{4{,}631}{2{,}105} \qquad = \quad 2.2{:}1$
(3) Asset turnover (net assets)	$\dfrac{\text{Revenue}}{\text{Total assets} - \text{current liabilities}}$	$\dfrac{32{,}400}{54{,}000 - 2{,}105} \quad = 0.6 \text{ times}$
(4) Gearing	$\dfrac{\text{Non-current liabilities}}{\text{Total equity} + \text{Non-current liabilities}} \times 100$	$\dfrac{1{,}495}{50{,}400 + 1{,}495} \quad = \quad 2.9\%$
(5) Interest cover	$\dfrac{\text{Profit from operations}}{\text{Finance costs}}$	$\dfrac{2{,}754}{459} \qquad = 6.0 \text{ times}$

Task 8

(a)

REPORT

To: Steve Horan
From: AAT student
Subject: Shareholding in Blenheim Ltd
Date: Today

As requested I have looked into the financial situation of Blenheim Ltd

(1) The **gross profit percentage** has deteriorated.

Less gross profit is being generated by sales/gross profit margin on sales.

Deterioration may be due to decreasing its sales price or increasing the cost of sales or both.

Could have been a change in the product mix.

(2) The **operating profit percentage** has improved.

More operating profit is being generated from sales – possibly an increase in sales volume.

Either an increase in the sales margins or a decrease in expenses, or both.

As the gross margins have deteriorated, must be the result of a decrease in expenses.

(3) The **inventory holding period** has deteriorated.

It now takes 18 days more to sell the inventory, on average, than it took the year before.

The increase might be due to slow moving inventory that might indicate possible obsolescence problems.

(4) The **trade receivables collection period** has deteriorated.

It now takes 15 days more to collect the debts, on average, than it took the year before.

It might be due to old debts which might become bad (irrecoverable) debts in the future.

(5) The **trade payables payment period** has deteriorated.

It now takes 8 days more to pay credit suppliers, on average, than it took the year before.

If trade payables are not paid on time they could refuse to supply further goods to the company.

(b)

Steve should be advised to consider selling his shares since only the operating profit percentage has improved. The use of resources needs to be urgently reviewed by management as the periods for inventory, trade receivables and trade payables have all deteriorated.

Before making a final decision he should seek further financial information from the company.

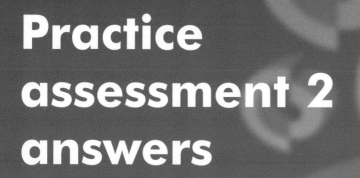

Practice assessment 2 answers

Task 1 (a)   **Kneale Ltd**
Reconciliation of profit from operations to net cash from operating activities

	£000
Profit from operations	1,780
Adjustments for:	
Depreciation	727
Gain on disposal of PPE	−112
Adjustment in respect of inventories	251
Adjustment in respect of trade receivables	−309
Adjustment in respect of trade payable	918
Cash generated by operations	3,255
Tax paid	−491
Interest paid	−693
Net cash from operating activities	2,071

(b)   **Kneale Ltd**
Statement of cash flows for the year ended 31 March 20X1

	£000
Net cash from operating activities	2,071
Investing activities	
Proceeds on disposal of PPE	185
Purchases of PPE	−2,085
Net cash used in investing activities	−1,900
Financing activities	
Bank loans repaid	−1,750
Proceeds of share issue	1,200
Dividends paid	−350
Net cash used in financing activities	−900
Net increase/decrease in cash and cash equivalents	−729
Cash and cash equivalents at beginning of year	312
Cash and cash equivalents at end of year	−417

Workings:

Proceeds on disposal of property, plant and equipment	£000
Carrying amount of PPE sold	73
Gain on disposal of PPE	112
Proceeds =	185

Purchases of property, plant and equipment	£000
PPE at start of year	6,325
Depreciation charge	−727
Carrying amount of PPE sold	−73
PPE at end of year	−7,610
Total property, plant and equipment additions =	−2,085

Task 2

Kneale Ltd – Statement of changes in equity for the year ended 31 March 20X1

	Share Capital	Other Reserves	Retained Earnings	Total Equity
	£000	£000	£000	£000
Balance at start of the year	1,500	210	6,043	7,753
Changes in equity for the year				
Profit for the year			873	873
Dividends			−350	−350
Issue of share capital	1,000	200		1,200
Balance at end of the year	2,500	410	6,566	9,476

Task 3(a) 1. relevance
             2. faithful representation

(b) **Relevance**

For information to be relevant it must:

- be capable of making a difference in the decisions made by users

- have predictive value, which helps users to predict future outcomes

- have confirmatory value, which helps users to confirm previous evaluations

Faithful representation

For the faithful representation of information it must:

- correspond to the effect of transactions or events

- as far as possible be complete (to include all information necessary for a user), neutral (without bias), and free from error (no errors in the description or process)

Task 4(a) An identifiable non-monetary asset without physical substance.

(b) 1. Computer software
        2. Patents

Note: other examples include copyrights, customer lists, licences and marketing rights

(c) 1. **Identifiability** – the asset is either separable from the entity and is capable of being sold or transferred, or it arises from contractual or other legal rights.

     2. **Control** – the entity has the power to obtain future economic benefits from the asset.

     3. **Future economic benefits** – includes revenue from the sale of products or services, cost savings, or other benefits.

Task 5(a) True
(b) £7,800
(c) at the lower of the fair value of the asset being leased and the present value of the minimum lease payments
(d) £20,400
(e) at the fair value of the consideration received or receivable
(f) 1 only

Task 6(a)

Severn Plc – Consolidated statement of financial position as at 31 March 20X1

	£000
ASSETS	
Non-current assets	
Goodwill	130
Property, plant and equipment	2,800
	2,930
Current assets	1,100
	1,100
Total assets	4,030
EQUITY AND LIABILITIES	
Equity	
Share capital	2,000
Retained earnings	686
Non-controlling interest	404
Total equity	3,090
Non-current liabilities	320
Current liabilities	620
Total liabilities	940
Total equity and liabilities	4,030

Workings

Goodwill	£000
Share capital – attributable to parent	–420
Retained earnings – attributable to parent	–150
Price paid	700
Goodwill =	130

Non-controlling interest (NCI)	£000
Share capital – attributable to NCI	280
Retained earnings – attributable to NCI	124
Non-controlling interest =	404

Retained earnings	£000
Parent	650
Subsidiary – attributable to parent	36
Retained earnings =	686

(b)

Sinton Plc – Consolidated statement of profit or loss for the year ended 31 March 20X1

	£000
Continuing operations	
Revenue	65,520
Cost of sales	–40,940
Gross profit	24,580
Other income	0
Distribution costs	–11,200
Administrative expenses	–5,200
Profit from operations	8,180
Finance costs	0
Profit before tax	8,180

Workings

Revenue	£000
Parent	48,400
Subsidiary	17,200
Total inter-company adjustment*	–80
Revenue =	65,520

Cost of sale	£000
Parent	31,200
Subsidiary	9,800
Total inter-company adjustment*	–60
Cost of sales =	40,940

* purchases –80, unrealised profit 20$^+$ = cost of sales –60

$^+$unrealised profit is deducted from closing inventories; the effect of this is to increase cost of sales (because closing inventories are deducted in the cost of sales calculation)

Distribution costs

£8,000,000 + £3,200,000 = £11,200,000

Administrative expenses

£4,200,000 + £1,000,000 = £5,200,000

Profit before tax

£5,500,000 + £3,200,000 – £500,000 inter-company dividend – £20,000 unrealised profit = £8,180,000

Task 7

Ratio	(a) Formula	(b) Calculation of ratio for Laceby Ltd
(1) Gross profit percentage	$\dfrac{\text{Gross profit} \times 100}{\text{Revenue}}$	$\dfrac{22,680 \times 100}{45,300}$ = 50.1%
(2) Acid test (quick) ratio	$\dfrac{\text{Current assets} - \text{inventories}}{\text{Current liabilities}}$	$\dfrac{8,022 - 2,514}{3,338}$ = 1.7:1
(3) Asset turnover (non-current assets)	$\dfrac{\text{Revenue}}{\text{Non-current assets}}$	$\dfrac{45,300}{77,094}$ = 0.6 times
(4) Inventory holding period (days)	$\dfrac{\text{Inventories}}{\text{Cost of sales}}$ x 365 days	$\dfrac{2,514}{22,620}$ x 365 = 40.6 days
(5) Trade payables payment period	$\dfrac{\text{Trade payables}}{\text{Cost of sales}}$ x 365 days	$\dfrac{2,715}{22,620}$ x 365 = 43.8 days

Task 8(a)

REPORT

To: Louise Forsythe
From: AAT student
Subject: Shareholding in Kingham Ltd
Date: Today

As requested I have looked into the financial situation of Kingham Ltd

(1) **Gross profit percentage** has deteriorated.

Less gross profit is being generated by sales/gross profit margin on sales.

Deterioration may be due to decreasing its sales price or increasing the cost of sales or both.

Could have been a change in the product mix.

(2) **Operating profit percentage** has improved.

More operating profit is being generated from sales – possibly an increase in sales volume.

Either an increase in the sales margins or a decrease in expenses, or both.

As the gross margins have deteriorated, must be the result of a decrease in expenses.

(3) **Return on shareholders' funds** has improved.

More profit after tax is being generated from shareholders' funds.

(4) **Gearing** has improved.

The company may have repaid loans during the year.

This makes it less risky.

Interest payments will be reduced.

Gives the company the ability to borrow in the future should it need to do so.

(5) **Interest cover** has improved.

More operating profit to cover interest payments.

This makes the company less risky.

Caused by higher operating profits/lower interest payments.

Lower interest payments could be due to loans being repaid (lower gearing) during the year.

(b)

Louise should be advised to consider maintaining her shares since, while gross profit percentage has deteriorated, operating profit percentage and return on shareholders' funds have both improved. The company is in a better financial position with reduced gearing and higher interest cover – both of these make the company less risky.

Before making a final decision she should seek further financial information from the company.

Practice assessment 3 answers

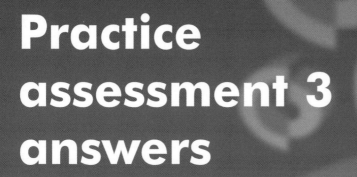

Task 1(a)

Chen Ltd

Reconciliation of profit from operations to net cash from operating activities

	£000
Profit from operations	9,774
Adjustments for:	
Depreciation	4,275
Dividends received	−84
Loss on disposal of PPE	40
Adjustment in respect of inventories	−1,672
Adjustment in respect of trade receivables	−309
Adjustment in respect of trade payables	−73
Cash generated by operations	11,951
Tax paid	−2,148
Interest paid	−212
Net cash from operating activities	9,591

(b)
Chen Ltd

Statement of cash flows for the year ended 31 March 20X1

	£000
Net cash from operating activities	9,591
Investing activities	
Dividends received	84
Proceeds on disposal of PPE	384
Purchases of PPE	−11,469
Net cash used in investing activities	−11,001
Financing activities	
Bank loans repaid	−1,750
Proceeds of share issue	3,000
Dividends paid	−554
Net cash from financing activities	696
Net increase/decrease in cash and cash equivalents	−714
Cash and cash equivalents at beginning of year	430
Cash and cash equivalents at end of year	−284

Workings

Proceeds on disposal of property, plant and equipment	*£000*
Carrying amount of PPE sold	424
Loss on disposal of PPE	–40
Proceeds =	384

Purchases of property, plant and equipment	*£000*
PPE at start of year	32,860
Depreciation charge	–4,275
Carrying amount of PPE sold	–424
PPE at end of year	–39,630
Total property, plant and equipment additions =	–11,469

Task 2

Chen Ltd – Statement of changes in equity for the year ended 31 March 20X1

	Share capital	Share premium	Retained earnings	Total equity
	£000	*£000*	*£000*	*£000*
Balance at 1 April 20X0	10,000	4,000	21,749	35,749
Changes in equity for 20X1				
Profit for the period			6,195	6,195
Dividends			–554	–554
Issue of share capital	2,000	1,000		3,000
Balance at 31 March 20X1	12,000	5,000	27,390	44,390

Task 3 (a)

The objective of general purpose financial reporting according to the IASB's *Conceptual Framework for Financial Reporting* is:

'to provide financial information about the reporting entity that is useful to existing and potential investors, lenders and other creditors in making decisions about providing resources to the entity.'

(b)

- **potential investors** – whether to buy shares in the company
- **existing investors** – whether to continue to hold, to sell, or to buy more shares in the company
- **lenders** – whether to make a loan to the company
- **other creditors** – whether to supply the company with goods or services

Task 4(a)

IAS 16 defines property, plant and equipment as 'tangible assets held for use in the production or supply of goods and services, which are expected to be used for more than one period'.

(b)

The two models are:

- the cost model, where the asset is carried at cost less accumulated depreciation and impairment losses
- the revaluation model, where the asset is carried on the statement of financial position at a revalued amount, being its fair value less any subsequent depreciation and impairment losses

(c)

A revaluation increase is credited directly within equity to a revaluation surplus – although an increase which reverses part or all of a previous decrease for the same asset is recognised as income in the statement of comprehensive income.

(d)

A revaluation decrease is recognised as an expense in the statement of comprehensive income – although a decrease which reverses part or all of a previous increase for the same asset is recognised in other comprehensive income and is debited to the revaluation surplus.

Task 5

- **(a)** False
- **(b)** All of them
- **(c)** 2 and 4
- **(d)** identifiability, future economic benefits, control
- **(e)** £27,000
- **(f)** £30,000

Task 6

Lee Plc – Consolidated statement of financial position as at 31 December 20X0

	£000
ASSETS	
Non-current assets	
Goodwill	940
Property, plant and equipment	6,365
	7,305
Current assets	3,187
Total assets	10,492
EQUITY AND LIABILITIES	
Equity	
Share capital	3,500
Share premium	750
Retained earnings	1,360
Non-controlling interest	810
Total equity	6,420
Non-current liabilities	405
Current liabilities	3,667
Total liabilities	4,072
Total equity and liabilities	10,492

Workings

Goodwill	£000
Share capital – attributable to parent	−1,500
Share premium – attributable to parent	−375
Revaluation reserve – attributable to parent	−150
Retained earnings – attributable to parent	−315
Price paid	3,400
Impairment	−120
Goodwill =	940

Non-controlling interest (NCI)	£000
Share capital – attributable to NCI	500
Share premium – attributable to NCI	125
Revaluation reserve – attributable to NCI	50
Retained earnings – attributable to NCI	135
Non-controlling interest =	810

Retained earnings	£000
Parent	1,390
Impairment	−120
Subsidiary – attributable to parent	90
Retained earnings =	1,360

Task 7

Ratio	(a) Formula	(b) Calculation of ratio for Dodia Ltd
(1) Operating profit percentage	$\dfrac{\text{Profit from operations}}{\text{Revenue}}$ x 100	$\dfrac{7{,}347}{64{,}300}$ x 100 = 11.4%
(2) Acid test (quick) ratio	$\dfrac{\text{Current assets} - \text{Inventories}}{\text{Current liabilities}}$	$\dfrac{9{,}338 - 3{,}695}{5{,}222}$ = 1.1:1
(3) Asset turnover (net assets)	$\dfrac{\text{Revenue}}{\text{Total assets} - \text{Current liabilities}}$	$\dfrac{64{,}300}{38{,}138 - 5{,}222}$ = 2.0 times
(4) Trade payables payment period	$\dfrac{\text{Trade payables}}{\text{Cost of sales}}$ x 365	$\dfrac{3{,}174}{39{,}163}$ x 365 = 29.6 days
(5) Interest cover	$\dfrac{\text{Profit from operations}}{\text{Finance costs}}$	$\dfrac{7{,}347}{1{,}054}$ = 7.0 times

Task 8

<table>
<tr><td>

email

To: joanna.fonseca@faloye.co.uk

From: aatstudent@fstmexam

Subject: Analysis of working capital and suggestions for improvement

Date: 15 April 20X2

</td></tr>
<tr><td>

As requested I have analysed the working capital of Faloye Limited by means of comparing four accounting ratios for the company with those of industry averages. My analysis is as follows:

(a)

Current ratio is worse

- Faloye Ltd has fewer current assets available to meet its current liabilities than the industry average.
- Looks to be too low which, on the face of it, may appear to suggest efficient management, but it could give problems in meeting current liabilities as they fall due.

Inventory holding period is worse

- Faloye Ltd is selling inventories more slowly than the industry average.
- Could be due to old/obsolete inventories/less demand from customers/poor inventory management systems.

Trade receivables collection period is better

- Faloye Ltd is collecting its receivables slightly quicker than the industry average.
- Could be due to shorter credit terms being offered, which may lead customers to look to other suppliers with better terms.

Trade payables payment period is longer – worse for supplier goodwill, but better for cash flow

- Faloye Ltd is paying trade payables slower than the industry average.
- While this is good for cash flow, it may lead to problems if suppliers press for payment.
- Not good for supplier goodwill.
- Faloye Ltd is unlikely to be able to take advantage of settlement discounts offered by suppliers.

(b)

Suggestions to improve management of working capital

- Increase turnover of inventory/reduce inventory levels, eg improve inventory control procedures, reduce selling prices.
- Further reduce trade receivable days, eg improve collection procedures, reduce credit periods, offer settlement discounts to encourage prompt payment.
- Formalise current terms with trade payables so as to avoid demands for immediate payment.

</td></tr>
</table>

Appendix

These pages may be photocopied for student use.

It is recommended that they are enlarged to A4 size.

These pages are also available for download from the Resources Section of www.osbornebooks.co.uk

The forms and formats are:

AAT Assessments for *Financial Statements* include a number of workings sheets to help with calculations. While it is not necessary to use the workings sheets to achieve full marks on a task, data in the workings will be taken into account if errors have been made in the financial statements.

In the AAT Assessment, some of the financial statements and all of the workings sheets feature lists of narrative items. In this Appendix the items are listed for you to choose from – not all will be needed in every task, and some may be 'distractors'. Note that, in AAT Assessments, the lists are tailored to specific tasks and could differ from those shown in this Appendix.

The following points should be noted when answering AAT Assessment tasks:

- negative amounts can be indicated by either minus signs or brackets

- commas can be used to indicate numbers in thousands, but can be omitted

- decimal points must always be indicated by a full stop

Statement of profit or loss and other comprehensive income for the year ended.................

	£000
Revenue	
Cost of sales	
Gross profit	
Distribution costs	
Administrative expenses	
Profit from operations	
Finance costs	
Profit before tax	
Tax	
Profit for the year from continuing operations	
Other comprehensive income for the year	
Total comprehensive income for the year	

Workings

Cost of sales	£000
Cost of sales =	

Select from the following list:

- Accruals
- Closing inventories
- Depreciation
- Opening inventories
- Prepayments
- Purchases

- -

Distribution costs	£000
Distribution costs =	

Select from the following list:

- Accruals
- Bad (irrecoverable) debts
- Depreciation
- Distribution costs
- Prepayments

Administrative expenses	£000
Administrative expenses =	

Select from the following list:

- Accruals
- Administrative expenses
- Bad debts
- Depreciation
- Prepayments

- -

Tax	£000
Tax =	

Select from the following list:

- Current year
- Previous year

Statement of changes in equity for the year ended . . . .

	Share capital £000	Other reserves £000	Retained earnings £000	Total equity £000
Balance at start of the year				
Changes in equity for the year				
Total comprehensive income*				
Dividends				
Issue of share capital				
Balance at end of year				

*'Profit for the year', if no other comprehensive income

Statement of financial position as at . . . .

	£000
Assets	
Non-current assets	
Current assets	
Total assets	
EQUITY AND LIABILITIES	
Equity	
Total equity	
Non-current liabilities	
Current liabilities	
Total liabilities	
Total equity and liabilities	

Select from the following list:

- Bank loans
- Cash and cash equivalents
- Debenture loans
- Inventories
- Property, plant and equipment
- Retained earnings

- Revaluation reserve
- Share capital
- Share premium
- Tax liability
- Trade and other payables
- Trade and other receivables

Workings

Property, plant and equipment	£000
Property, plant and equipment =	

Select from the following list:

- Accumulated depn – land and buildings
- Accumulated depn – plant and equipment
- Land and buildings – value
- Plant and equipment – cost
- Revaluation – land and buildings

- -

Trade and other receivables	£000
Trade and other receivables =	

Select from the following list

- Accruals – trial balance
- Additional costs/expenses prepaid
- Prepayments – trial balance
- Trade and other receivables
- Additional costs/expenses accrued
- Bad (irrecoverable) debt
- Trade and other payables

Trade and other payables	£000
Trade and other payables =	

Select from the following list:

- Accruals – trial balance
- Additional costs/expenses prepaid
- Prepayments – trial balance
- Trade and other payables
- Additional costs/expenses accrued
- Dividends
- Taxation liability
- Trade and other receivables

- -

Retained earnings	£000
Retained earnings =	

Select from the following list:

- Dividends paid
- Other comprehensive income for the year
- Retained earnings at start of the year
- Revaluation reserve
- Total comprehensive income for the year
- Total profit for the year

Revaluation reserve	£000
Revaluation reserve =	

Select from the following list:

- Dividends paid
- Other comprehensive income for the year
- Retained earnings at start of the year
- Revaluation reserve at start of the year
- Total comprehensive income for the year
- Total profit for the year

Reconciliation of profits from operations to net cash from operating activities

	£000
Profit from operations	
Adjustments for:	
Cash generated by operations	
Net cash from operations	

Select from the following list:

- Adjustment in respect of inventories
- Adjustment in respect of trade payables
- Adjustment in respect of trade receivables
- Depreciation
- Dividends received
- Gain/loss on disposal of PPE
- Interest paid
- New bank loans
- Proceeds on disposal of PPE
- Profit after tax
- Profit before tax
- Profit from operations
- Purchases of PPE
- Tax paid

Statement of cash flows for the year ended . . . .

	£000
Net cash from operating activities	
Investing activities	
Net cash used in/from investing activities	
Financing activities	
Net cash used in/from financing activities	
Net increase/decrease in cash and cash equivalents	
Cash and cash equivalents at beginning of year	
Cash and cash equivalents at end of year	

Select from the following list:

- Adjustment in respect of inventories
- Adjustment in respect of trade payables
- Adjustment in respect of trade receivables
- Bank loans repaid
- Dividends paid
- Dividends received
- New bank loans
- Proceeds of share issue
- Proceeds on disposal of PPE
- Purchases of PPE

Workings

Proceeds on disposal of property, plant and equipment	*£000*
Proceeds =	

Select from the following list:

- Carrying amount of PPE sold
- Depreciation charge
- Gain/loss on disposal of PPE
- PPE at end of year
- PPE at start of year

- -

Purchases of property, plant and equipment	*£000*
Total property, plant and equipment additions =	

Select from the following list:

- Carrying amount of PPE sold
- Depreciation charge
- Gain/loss on disposal of PPE
- PPE at end of year
- PPE at start of year

Consolidated statement of profit or loss for the year ended . . . .

	£000
Continuing operations	
Revenue	
Cost of sales	
Gross profit	
Other income	
Distribution costs	
Administrative expenses	
Profit from operations	
Finance costs	
Profit before tax	
Tax	
Profit for the period from continuing operations	

Attributable to	£000
Equity holders of the parent	
Non-controlling interest	
Profit for the period from continuing operations =	

Workings

Revenue	£000
Parent	
Subsidiary	
Total inter-company adjustment*	
Revenue =	

* enter '0' if no adjustment needed

Cost of sales	£000
Parent	
Subsidiary	
Total inter-company adjustment*	
Cost of sales =	

* enter '0' if no adjustment needed

Consolidated statement of financial position as at . . . .

	£000
ASSETS	
Non-current assets	
Goodwill	
Property, plant and equipment	
Current assets	
Inventories	
Trade receivables	
Cash and cash equivalents	
Total assets	
EQUITY AND LIABILITIES	
Equity	
Share capital	
Share premium	
Retained earnings	
Non-controlling interest	
Total equity	
Non-current liabilities	
Current liabilities	
Total liabilities	
Total equity and liabilities	

Workings

Goodwill	£000
Goodwill =	

Select from the following list:

- Impairment
- Retained earnings – attributable to parent
- Share capital – attributable to parent

- Price paid
- Revaluation reserve – attributable to parent
- Share premium – attributable to parent

- -

Non-controlling interest (NCI)	£000
Non-controlling interest =	

Select from the following list:

- Current assets – attributable to NCI
- Non-current assets – attributable to NCI
- Retained earnings – attributable to NCI
- Share capital – attributable to NCI

- Impairment
- Price paid
- Revaluation reserve – attributable to NCI
- Share premium – attributable to NCI

Retained earnings	£000
Retained earnings =	

Select from the following list:

- Impairment
- Parent
- Revaluation
- Subsidiary – attributable to parent

for your notes

for your notes